Basic Computation

Working with Circles and Volume

Loretta M. Taylor, Ed. D.
Mathematics Teacher
Hillsdale High School
San Mateo, California

Harold D. Taylor, Ed. D.
Head, Mathematics Department
Aragon High School
San Mateo, California

DALE
SEYMOUR
PUBLICATIONS
P.O. BOX 10888
PALO ALTO, CA 94303

Editors: Elaine C. Murphy, Susan McCalla
Production Coordinator: Ruth Cottrell
Cover designer: Michael Rogondino
Compositor: WB Associates
Printer: Malloy Lithographing

ISBN 0-86651-007-9

Order Number DS01188

defghi-MA-8932109

DALE
SEYMOUR
PUBLICATIONS
P.O. BOX 10888
PALO ALTO, CA 94303

ABOUT THE PROGRAM

WHAT IS THE BASIC COMPUTATION LIBRARY?

The books in the BASIC COMPUTATION library together provide comprehensive practice in all the essential computational skills. There are practice books and a test book. The practice books consist of carefully sequenced drill worksheets organized in groups of five. The test book contains daily quizzes (160 quizzes in all), semester tests, and year-end tests written in standardized-test formats.

If you find this book effective, you may want to use others in the series. Build your own library to suit your own needs.

BOOK 1	WORKING WITH WHOLE NUMBERS
BOOK 2	UNDERSTANDING FRACTIONS
BOOK 3	WORKING WITH FRACTIONS
BOOK 4	WORKING WITH DECIMALS
BOOK 5	WORKING WITH PERCENTS
BOOK 6	UNDERSTANDING MEASUREMENT
BOOK 7	FINDING AREA AND PERIMETER
BOOK 8	WORKING WITH CIRCLES AND VOLUME
BOOK 9	APPLYING COMPUTATIONAL SKILLS
TEST BOOK	BASIC COMPUTATION QUIZZES AND TESTS

WHO CAN USE THE BASIC COMPUTATION LIBRARY?

Classroom teachers, substitute teachers, tutors, parents, and persons wishing to study on their own can use these materials. Although written specifically for the general math classroom, books in the BASIC COMPUTATION library can be used with any program requiring carefully sequenced computational practice. The material is appropriate for use with any person, young or old, who has not yet certified computational proficiency. It is especially suitable for middle school, junior high school, and high school students who need to master the essential computational skills necessary for mathematical literacy.

WHAT IS IN THIS BOOK?

This book is a practice book. In addition to these teacher notes, it contains student worksheets, example problems, and a record form.

Worksheets

The worksheets are designed to give even the slowest student a chance to master the essential computational skills. Most worksheets come in five equivalent forms allowing for pretesting, practice, and posttesting on any one skill. Each set of worksheets provides practice in only one or two specific skills and the work progresses in very small steps from one set to the next. Instructions are clear and simple, with handwritten samples of the exercises completed. Ample practice is provided on each page, giving students the opportunity to strengthen their skills. Answers to each problem are included in the back of the book.

Example Problems

Fully-worked examples show how to work each type of exercise. Examples are keyed to the worksheet pages. The example solutions are written in a straightforward manner and are easily understood.

Record Form

A record form is provided to help in recording progress and assessing instructional needs.

Answers

Answers to each problem are included in the back of the book.

HOW CAN THE BASIC COMPUTATION LIBRARY BE USED?

The materials in the BASIC COMPUTATION library can serve as the major skeleton of a skills program or as supplements to any other computational skills program. The large number of worksheets gives a wide variety from which to choose and allows flexibility in structuring a program to meet individual needs. The following suggestions are offered to show how the BASIC COMPUTATION library may be adapted to a particular situation.

Minimal Competency Practice

In various fields and schools, standardized tests are used for entrance, passage from one level to another, and certification of competency or proficiency prior to graduation. The materials in the BASIC COMPUTATION library are particularly well-suited to preparing for any of the various mathematics competency tests, including the mathematics portion of the General Educational Development test (GED) used to certify high school equivalency.

Together, the books in the BASIC COMPUTATION library give practice in all the essential computational skills measured on competency tests. The semester tests and year-end tests from the test book are written in standardized-test formats. These tests can be used as sample minimal competency tests. The worksheets can be used to brush up on skills measured by the competency tests.

Skill Maintenance

Since most worksheets come in five equivalent forms, the computation work can be organized into weekly units as suggested by the following schedule. Day one is for pretesting and introducing a skill. The next three days are for drill and practice followed by a unit test on the fifth day.

AUTHORS' SUGGESTED TEACHING SCHEDULE

	Day 1	Day 2	Day 3	Day 4	Day 5
Week 1	pages 1 and 2 pages 11 and 12	pages 3 and 4 pages 13 and 14	pages 5 and 6 pages 15 and 16	pages 7 and 8 pages 17 and 18	pages 9 and 10 pages 19 and 20
Week 2	pages 21 and 22 pages 31 and 32	pages 23 and 24 pages 33 and 34	pages 25 and 26 pages 35 and 36	pages 27 and 28 pages 37 and 38	pages 29 and 30 pages 39 and 40
Week 3	pages 41 and 42 pages 51 and 52	pages 43 and 44 pages 53 and 54	pages 45 and 46 pages 55 and 56	pages 47 and 48 pages 57 and 58	pages 49 and 50 pages 59 and 60
Week 4	pages 61 and 62	pages 63 and 64	pages 65 and 66	pages 67 and 68	pages 69 and 70

The daily quizzes from BASIC COMPUTATION QUIZZES AND TESTS can be used on the drill and practice days for maintenance of previously-learned skills or diagnosis of skill deficiencies.

A five-day schedule can begin on any day of the week. The authors' ideal schedule begins on Thursday, with reteaching on Friday. Monday and Tuesday are for touch-up teaching and individualized instruction. Wednesday is test day.

Supplementary Drill

There are more than 18,000 problems in the BASIC COMPUTATION library. When students need more practice with a given skill, use the appropriate worksheets from the library. They are suitable for classwork or homework practice following the teaching of a specific skill. With five equivalent pages for most worksheets, adequate practice is provided for each essential skill.

HOW ARE MATERIALS PREPARED?

The books are designed so the pages can be easily removed and reproduced by Thermofax, Xerox, or a similar process. For example, a ditto master can be made on a Thermofax for use on a spirit duplicator. Permanent transparencies can be made by processing special transparencies through a Thermofax or Xerox.

Any system will run more smoothly if work is stored in folders. Record forms can be attached to the folders so that either students or teachers can keep records of individual progress. Materials stored in this way are readily available for conferences.

EXAMPLE PROBLEMS

ENGLISH UNITS FOR CUBES

EXAMPLE 1 Find the volume V and the surface area S of a cube with edge $e = 4$ in.

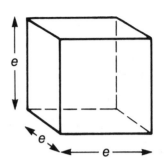

Solution: $V = e^3$

$\qquad = 4^3$

$\qquad = 64$

The volume is 64 in.^{3}.

$S = 6e^2$

$\quad = 6(4^2)$

$\quad = 6(16)$

$\quad = 96$

The surface area is 96 in.^{2}.

METRIC UNITS FOR CUBES

EXAMPLE 1 Find the volume V and the surface area S of a cube with edge $e = 19$ cm.

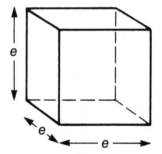

Solution: $V = e^3$

$\qquad = 19^3$

$\qquad = 6859$

The volume is 6859 cm^3.

$S = 6e^2$

$\quad = 6(19^2)$

$\quad = 6(361)$

$\quad = 2166$

The surface area is 2166 cm^2.

ENGLISH UNITS FOR RECTANGULAR PRISMS

EXAMPLE 1 Find the volume V and the surface area S of a rectangular prism with length $l = 8$ ft, width $w = 6$ ft, and height $h = 5$ ft.

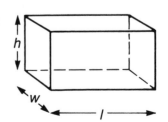

Solution: $V = lwh$

$\qquad = 8 \times 6 \times 5$

$\qquad = 240$

The volume is 240 ft^3.

v

$$S = 2lw + 2hw + 2hl$$
$$= 2(8)(6) + 2(5)(6) + 2(5)(8)$$
$$= 96 + 60 + 80$$
$$= 236$$

The surface area is 236 ft².

METRIC UNITS FOR RECTANGULAR PRISMS

EXAMPLE   Find the volume V and the surface area S of a rectangular prism with length $l = 14$ m, width $w = 8$ m, and height $h = 5$ m.

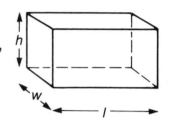

Solution: $V = lwh$
$$= 14 \times 8 \times 5$$
$$= 560$$

The volume is 560 m³.

$$S = 2lw + 2hw + 2hl$$
$$= 2(14)(8) + 2(5)(8) + 2(5)(14)$$
$$= 224 + 80 + 140$$
$$= 444$$

The surface area is 444 m².

VOLUME AND SURFACE AREA OF RECTANGULAR PRISMS

EXAMPLE   A hole in a gravel pit measures 90 yards by 80 yards by 12 yards. How many cubic yards of gravel have been removed?

Solution: Find the volume of the hole.

$$V = lwh$$
$$= 90 \times 80 \times 12$$
$$= 86,400$$

86,400 yd³ have been removed.

MORE VOLUME AND SURFACE AREA OF RECTANGULAR PRISMS

EXAMPLE   A package is in the shape of a rectangular prism. The dimensions are 18 inches by 14 inches by 10 inches. How many square inches of paper are needed to cover it?

Solution: Find the surface area of the package.

$$S = 2lw + 2hw + 2hl$$
$$= 2(18)(14) + 2(10)(14) + 2(10)(18)$$
$$= 504 + 280 + 360$$
$$= 1144$$

1144 in.² of paper are needed.

ENGLISH UNITS FOR TRIANGULAR PRISMS AND PYRAMIDS

EXAMPLE 1 Find the volume of a triangular prism with the triangular faces having altitude a = 4 in. and base b = 9 in., and height h of the prism = 3 in.

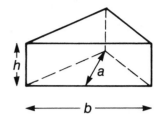

Solution: $V = \frac{1}{2}abh$

$\qquad = \frac{1}{2}(4)(9)(3)$

$\qquad = 54$

The volume is 54 in.³.

EXAMPLE 2 Find the volume of a triangular pyramid with the triangular base having altitude a = 2 ft and base b = 7 ft, and height h of the pyramid = 3 ft.

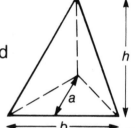

Solution: $V = \frac{1}{6}abh$

$\qquad = \frac{1}{6}(2)(7)(3)$

$\qquad = 7$

The volume is 7 ft³.

METRIC UNITS FOR TRIANGULAR PRISMS AND PYRAMIDS

EXAMPLE 1 Find the volume of a triangular prism with the triangular faces having altitude a = 13 cm and base b = 28 cm, and height h of the prism = 8 cm.

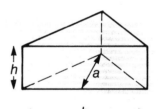

Solution: $V = \frac{1}{2}abh$

$\qquad = \frac{1}{2}(13)(28)(8)$

$\qquad = 1456$

The volume is 1456 cm³.

EXAMPLE 2 Find the volume of a triangular pyramid with the triangular base having altitude a = 14 mm and base b = 30 mm, and height h of the pyramid = 26 mm.

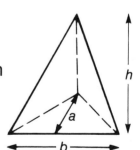

Solution: $V = \frac{1}{6}abh$

$\qquad = \frac{1}{6}(14)(30)(26)$

$\qquad = 1820$

The volume is 1820 mm³.

MEASURING CIRCLES

EXAMPLE 1 Use a flexible ruler to measure the circumference
and diameter of the circle to the nearest
millimeter. Write the ratio of circumference to
diameter first as a fraction, then as a decimal
to the nearest hundredth.

Solution: circumference = 69 mm
diameter = 22 mm

$$\frac{\text{circumference}}{\text{diameter}} = \frac{69}{22} \approx 3.14$$

MORE MEASURING CIRCLES

EXAMPLE 1 Measure the diameter of the circle to the nearest
millimeter. Then find r, C, and A, if $r = \frac{1}{2}d$,
$C = \pi d$, and $A = \pi r^2$. Use 3.14 for π.

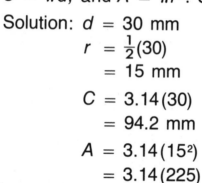

Solution: d = 30 mm
$r = \frac{1}{2}(30)$
= 15 mm

C = 3.14(30)
= 94.2 mm

A = 3.14(15²)
= 3.14(225)
= 706.5 mm²

CIRCUMFERENCE AND AREA OF CIRCLES

EXAMPLE 1 Find the diameter, circumference, and area of a circle having
radius = 12.2. Use 3.14 for π.

Solution: $d = 2r$
= 2(12.2)
= 24.4

$C = \pi d$
= 3.14(24.4)
= 76.616

$A = \pi r^2$
= 3.14(12.2²)
= 3.14(148.84)
= 467.3576

USING CIRCLES

EXAMPLE   Three people share a pizza with a diameter 12 inches. How many square inches of pizza does each person get?

Solution: Find the area of the pizza, then divide by 3.

$$A = \pi r^2$$
$$= 3.14\,(6^2)$$
$$= 3.14\,(36)$$
$$= 113.04 \text{ in.}^2$$

$$\frac{A}{3} = \frac{113.04}{3}$$
$$= 37.68 \text{ in.}^2$$

VOLUME AND SURFACE AREA OF CYLINDERS

EXAMPLE   Find the volume and surface area of a cylinder with height 12 cm and radius of the base 10 cm. Use 3.14 for π.

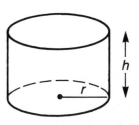

Solution: $V = \pi r^2 h$
$$= 3.14\,(10^2)\,(12)$$
$$= 3.14\,(100)\,(12)$$
$$= 3768$$

The volume is 3768 cm³.

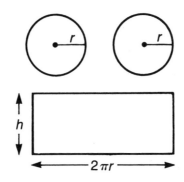

$$S = 2\pi r^2 + 2\pi rh$$
$$= 2\,(3.14)\,(10^2) + 2\,(3.14)\,(10)\,(12)$$
$$= 1381.6$$

The surface area is 1381.6 cm².

VOLUME OF CONES AND SPHERES

EXAMPLE 1 Find the volume of a cone with height 27 cm and radius of the base 19 cm. Use 3.14 for π.

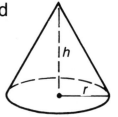

Solution: $V = \frac{1}{3}\pi r^2 h$

$\quad\quad\quad\quad = \frac{1}{3}(3.14)(19^2)(27)$

$\quad\quad\quad\quad = 10{,}201.86$

The volume is 10,201.86 cm³.

EXAMPLE 2 Find the volume of a sphere with radius 21 mm. Use 3.14 for π.

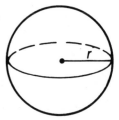

Solution: $V = \frac{4}{3}\pi r^3$

$\quad\quad\quad\quad = \frac{4}{3}(3.14)(21^3)$

$\quad\quad\quad\quad = 38{,}772.72$

The volume is 38,772.72 mm³.

STUDENT RECORD SHEET

Worksheets Completed

Page Number

1	3	5	7	9
2	4	6	8	10
11	13	15	17	19
12	14	16	18	20
21	23	25	27	29
22	24	26	28	30
31	33	35	37	39
32	34	36	38	40
41	43	45	47	49
42	44	46	48	50
51	53	55	57	59
52	54	56	58	60
61	63	65	67	69
62	64	66	68	70

Daily Quiz Grades

No.	Score

Check List Skill Mastered

	Skill	Date
☐	English units for cubes	
☐	metric units for cubes	
☐	English units for rectangular prisms	
☐	metric units for rectangular prisms	
☐	volume & surface area of rectangular prisms	
☐	English units for triangular prisms & pyramids	
☐	metric units for triangular prisms & pyramids	
☐	measuring circles	
☐	circumference & area of circles	
☐	using circles	
☐	volume & surface area of cylinders	
☐	volume of cones & spheres	

Notes

_____

_____

_____

_____

_____

_____

_____

Use this page to make flexible rulers.

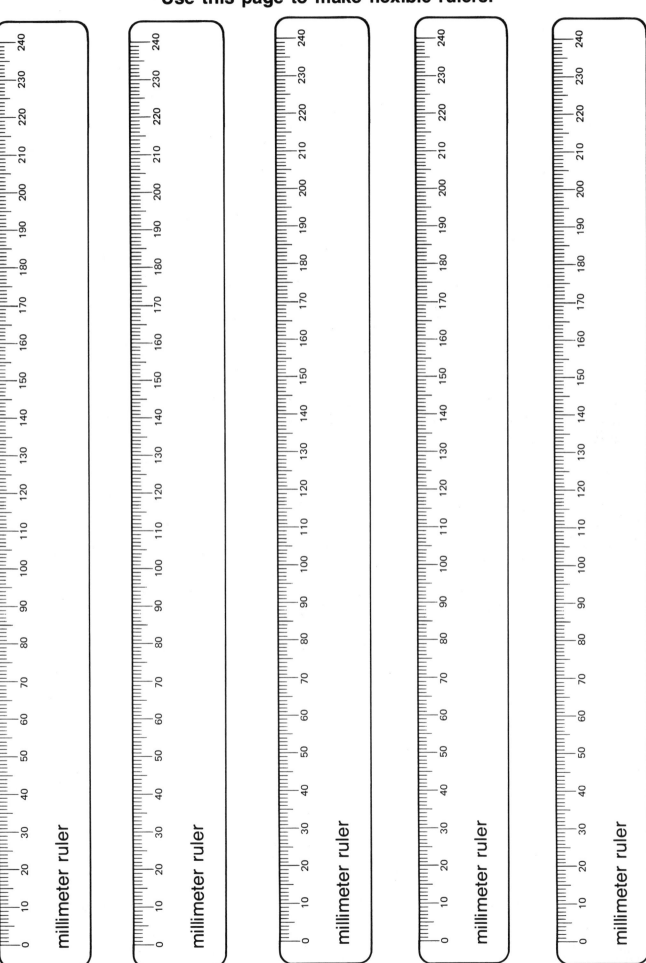

millimeter ruler

millimeter ruler

millimeter ruler

millimeter ruler

millimeter ruler

English units for cubes

Name _____

Date _____

Complete the following chart.
Use $V = e^3$ for volume and $S = 6e^2$ for surface area.
Be sure to write units in your answers.

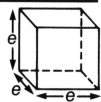

	e	V	S
1.	5 ft	$125\,ft^3$	$150\,ft^2$
2.	23 yd		
3.	12 in.		
4.	28 in.		
5.	22 ft		
6.	$\frac{1}{4}$ in.		
7.	$\frac{2}{3}$ ft		
8.	$\frac{3}{4}$ yd		
9.	$\frac{5}{16}$ in.		
10.	$\frac{5}{6}$ ft		
11.	$\frac{3}{8}$ in.		
12.	$\frac{7}{8}$ in.		
13.	$2\frac{1}{6}$ in.		
14.	$1\frac{7}{12}$ yd		
15.	$3\frac{1}{4}$ ft		
16.			$150\,yd^2$
17.			$96\,in.^2$
18.		$8\,ft^3$	
19.		$27\,in.^3$	
20.			$24\,ft^2$

1

Metric units for cubes

Name _____

Date _____

Complete the following chart.
Use $V = e^3$ for volume and $S = 6e^2$ for surface area.
Be sure to write units in your answers.

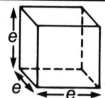

	e	V	S
1.	9 m	$729\,m^3$	$486\,m^2$
2.	13 cm		
3.	70 mm		
4.	14 cm		
5.	0.7 mm		
6.	1.2 cm		
7.	3.8 m		
8.	9.2 dm		
9.			54 cm²
10.		125 cm³	

English units for cubes

Name _____

Date _____

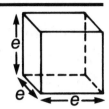

Complete the following chart.
Use $V = e^3$ for volume and $S = 6e^2$ for surface area.
Be sure to write units in your answers.

	e	V	S
1.	17 in.	4913 in.^{3}	1734 in.^{2}
2.	11 in.		
3.	29 ft		
4.	40 in.		
5.	25 yd		
6.	100 in.		
7.	3 yd		
8.	$\frac{5}{16}$ in.		
9.	$\frac{3}{4}$ in.		
10.	$\frac{5}{12}$ ft		
11.	$\frac{9}{16}$ in.		
12.	$\frac{5}{6}$ yd		
13.	$\frac{7}{12}$ ft		
14.	$\frac{1}{4}$ yd		
15.	$7\frac{3}{4}$ in.		
16.	$2\frac{2}{3}$ yd		
17.	$4\frac{3}{4}$ ft		
18.			384 ft^2
19.			1014 in.^{2}
20.		64 yd^3	

Metric units for cubes

Name _____

Date _____

Complete the following chart.
Use $V = e^3$ for volume and $S = 6e^2$ for surface area.
Be sure to write units in your answers.

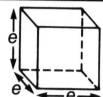

	e	V	S
1.	4 m	64 m³	96 m²
2.	44 cm		
3.	37 mm		
4.	0.2 cm		
5.	7.3 m		
6.	3.2 mm		
7.	4.1 cm		
8.	5.7 m		
9.			864 mm²
10.		512 cm³	

4

English units for cubes

Name _____

Date _____

Complete the following chart.
Use $V = e^3$ for volume and $S = 6e^2$ for surface area.
Be sure to write units in your answers.

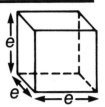

	e	V	S
1.	15 in.	3375 in.^{3}	1350 in.^{2}
2.	43 yd		
3.	6 ft		
4.	18 ft		
5.	90 yd		
6.	30 in.		
7.	$\frac{3}{16}$ in.		
8.	$\frac{7}{12}$ yd		
9.	$\frac{11}{12}$ ft		
10.	$\frac{5}{8}$ in.		
11.	$\frac{7}{16}$ in.		
12.	$\frac{3}{4}$ ft		
13.	$\frac{5}{6}$ yd		
14.	$1\frac{3}{4}$ yd		
15.	$3\frac{7}{8}$ in.		
16.	$2\frac{5}{9}$ yd		
17.			1176 in.^{2}
18.			216 yd^2
19.		27 in.^{3}	
20.		8 in.^{3}	

Metric units for cubes

Complete the following chart.
Use $V = e^3$ for volume and $S = 6e^2$ for surface area.
Be sure to write units in your answers.

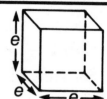

	e	V	S
1.	35 m	42,875 m³	7350 m²
2.	21 cm		
3.	42 mm		
4.	4.7 cm		
5.	5.1 m		
6.	7.5 cm		
7.	0.8 m		
8.	6.3 mm		
9.			600 cm²
10.		343 cm³	

6

English units for cubes

Name _____

Date _____

Complete the following chart.

Use $V = e^3$ for volume and $S = 6e^2$ for surface area.

Be sure to write units in your answers.

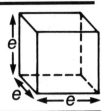

	e	V	S
1.	41 ft	68,921 ft³	10,086 ft²
2.	20 yd		
3.	38 ft		
4.	60 yd		
5.	2 in.		
6.	32 in.		
7.	$\frac{9}{16}$ in.		
8.	$\frac{1}{4}$ yd		
9.	$\frac{1}{12}$ ft		
10.	$\frac{5}{6}$ ft		
11.	$\frac{5}{12}$ ft		
12.	$\frac{7}{9}$ yd		
13.	$\frac{3}{8}$ in.		
14.	$3\frac{3}{4}$ yd		
15.	$1\frac{5}{8}$ in.		
16.	$5\frac{2}{3}$ ft		
17.			1350 in.²
18.		1 ft³	
19.		64 in.³	
20.			726 ft²

Metric units for cubes

Complete the following chart.

Use $V = e^3$ for volume and $S = 6e^2$ for surface area.

Be sure to write units in your answers.

	e	V	S
1.	8 m	512 m³	384 cm²
2.	33 cm		
3.	27 mm		
4.	4.3 m		
5.	0.5 mm		
6.	2.8 cm		
7.	9.4 mm		
8.			24 m²
9.			486 cm²
10.		1000 cm³	

English units for cubes

Name _____

Date _____

Complete the following chart.
Use $V = e^3$ for volume and $S = 6e^2$ for surface area.
Be sure to write units in your answers.

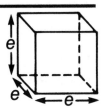

	e	V	S
1.	10 ft	1000 ft³	600 ft²
2.	31 yd		
3.	7 in.		
4.	39 ft		
5.	50 yd		
6.	90 in.		
7.	$\frac{3}{4}$ yd		
8.	$\frac{1}{6}$ yd		
9.	$\frac{7}{8}$ in.		
10.	$\frac{11}{16}$ in.		
11.	$\frac{11}{12}$ ft		
12.	$\frac{7}{12}$ ft		
13.	$\frac{1}{4}$ yd		
14.	$2\frac{1}{3}$ ft		
15.	$2\frac{3}{4}$ in.		
16.	$1\frac{5}{6}$ yd		
17.			6 yd²
18.			294 in.²
19.		1331 yd³	
20.		125 ft³	

Metric units for cubes

Name _____

Date _____

Complete the following chart.
Use $V = e^3$ for volume and $S = 6e^2$ for surface area.
Be sure to write units in your answers.

	e	V	S
1.	26 cm	17,576 cm³	4056 cm²
2.	16 m		
3.	34 cm		
4.	2.1 cm		
5.	0.6 m		
6.	6.4 mm		
7.	8.2 cm		
8.	7.3 m		
9.			726 cm²
10.		729 m³	

10

English units for rectangular prisms

Name _____

Date _____

Complete the following.
Use $V = lwh$ and $S = 2lw + 2hw + 2hl$.
Be sure to write units in your answers.

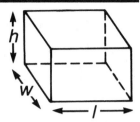

	l	w	h	V	S
1.	5 ft	3 ft	4 ft	60 ft³	94 ft²
2.	27 in.	12 in.	10 in.		
3.	$\frac{3}{4}$ ft	$\frac{2}{3}$ ft	$\frac{5}{12}$ ft		
4.	$2\frac{1}{4}$ in.	$3\frac{5}{8}$ in.	$1\frac{3}{4}$ in.		
5.	$4\frac{2}{3}$ yd	$7\frac{1}{4}$ yd	$1\frac{5}{6}$ yd		
6.	$3\frac{1}{2}$ ft	$1\frac{1}{2}$ ft	$1\frac{1}{2}$ ft		
7.		34 in.	22 in.	37,400 in.³	
8.	17 ft		14 ft	3808 ft³	

11

Name _____

Date _____

Complete the following.
Use $V = lwh$ and $S = 2lw + 2hw + 2hl$.
Be sure to write units in your answers.

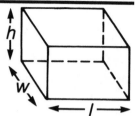

	l	w	h	V	S
1.	7 cm	3 cm	6 cm	$126 cm^3$	$162 cm^2$
2.	85 m	55 m	17 m		
3.	8.2 cm	5.3 cm	1.4 cm		
4.	0.62 m	0.51 m	0.28 m		
5.	9.3 dm	8.2 dm	3.8 dm		
6.	3.5 mm	2.8 mm	1.3 mm		
7.	13 m	5 m		$585 m^3$	

English units for rectangular prisms

Name _____

Date _____

Complete the following.
Use $V = lwh$ and $S = 2lw + 2hw + 2hl$.
Be sure to write units in your answers.

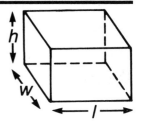

	l	w	h	V	S
1.	4 in.	2 in.	7 in.	56 in.^{3}	100 in.^{2}
2.	8 ft	4 ft	2 ft		
3.	42 in.	24 in.	15 in.		
4.	$\frac{3}{4}$ in.	$\frac{1}{4}$ in.	$\frac{5}{8}$ in.		
5.	$3\frac{3}{4}$ ft	$2\frac{2}{3}$ ft	$1\frac{5}{6}$ ft		
6.	$2\frac{5}{6}$ yd	$3\frac{3}{4}$ yd	$4\frac{2}{3}$ yd		
7.	$7\frac{1}{2}$ in.	$6\frac{3}{4}$ in.	$2\frac{1}{4}$ in.		
8.		28 ft	14 ft	12,544 ft^3	
9.	16 yd		5 yd	960 yd^3	

Metric units for rectangular prisms

Name _____

Date _____

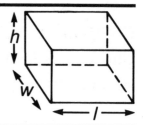

Complete the following.
Use $V = lwh$ and $S = 2lw + 2hw + 2hl$.
Be sure to write units in your answers.

	l	w	h	V	S
1.	23 m	13 m	12 m	3588 m^3	1462 m^2
2.	5.3 cm	4.2 cm	3.1 cm		
3.	0.78 m	0.63 m	0.41 m		
4.	3.6 cm	2.1 cm	1.3 cm		
5.	4.9 m	3.6 m	2.2 m		
6.	15 cm	8 cm		720 cm^3	
7.	12 m	4 m		336 m^3	

14

English units for rectangular prisms

Name _____

Date _____

Complete the following.
Use $V = lwh$ and $S = 2lw + 2hw + 2hl$.
Be sure to write units in your answers.

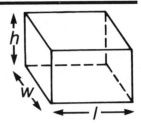

	l	*w*	*h*	*V*	*S*
1.	6 ft	1 ft	5 ft	30 ft³	82 ft²
2.	9 yd	3 yd	6 yd		
3.	56 in.	19 in.	16 in.		
4.	$\frac{2}{3}$ ft	$\frac{1}{6}$ ft	$\frac{1}{3}$ ft		
5.	$5\frac{7}{8}$ in.	$3\frac{1}{4}$ in.	$2\frac{3}{4}$ in.		
6.	$4\frac{1}{3}$ ft	$2\frac{1}{6}$ ft	$4\frac{1}{4}$ ft		
7.	$8\frac{2}{3}$ yd	$5\frac{1}{4}$ yd	$2\frac{2}{3}$ yd		
8.	24 in.		17 in.	7344 in.³	

15

Metric units for rectangular prisms

Name _____

Date _____

Complete the following.
Use $V = lwh$ and $S = 2lw + 2hw + 2hl$.
Be sure to write units in your answers.

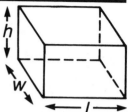

	l	*w*	*h*	*V*	*S*
1.	37 cm	28 cm	21 cm	21,756 cm³	4802 cm²
2.	7.6 m	3.5 m	2.2 m		
3.	0.69 cm	0.32 cm	0.55 cm		
4.	4.2 m	3.7 m	1.4 m		
5.	5.8 mm	3.2 mm	2.3 mm		
6.	22 mm	13 mm		2002 mm³	
7.		21 m	14 m	12,642 m³	

16

English units for rectangular prisms

Name _____

Date _____

Complete the following.
Use $V = lwh$ and $S = 2lw + 2hw + 2hl$.
Be sure to write units in your answers.

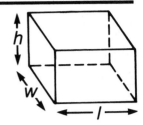

	l	*w*	*h*	*V*	*S*
1.	7 ft	3 ft	4 ft	84 ft³	122 ft²
2.	8 yd	1 yd	3 yd		
3.	51 in.	17 in.	11 in.		
4.	$\frac{5}{6}$ ft	$\frac{3}{4}$ ft	$\frac{2}{3}$ ft		
5.	$4\frac{2}{3}$ yd	$3\frac{3}{4}$ yd	$5\frac{1}{3}$ yd		
6.	$5\frac{5}{8}$ in.	$4\frac{3}{4}$ in.	$1\frac{1}{4}$ in.		
7.	$3\frac{1}{2}$ ft	$4\frac{1}{3}$ ft	$2\frac{1}{3}$ ft		
8.	13 in.	11 in.		1144 in.³	
9.	31 ft		18 ft	12,834 ft³	

17

Metric units for rectangular prisms

Name _____

Date _____

Complete the following.

Use $V = lwh$ and $S = 2lw + 2hw + 2hl$.

Be sure to write units in your answers.

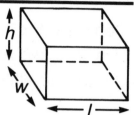

	l	w	h	V	S
1.	23 cm	12 cm	14 cm	3864 cm³	1532 cm²
2.	8.1 m	6.3 m	1.8 m		
3.	0.37 m	0.25 m	0.16 m		
4.	6.7 cm	5.3 cm	2.3 cm		
5.	5.6 mm	4.1 mm	3.7 mm		
6.		16 cm	13 cm	5200 cm³	
7.	9.2 mm	8.3 mm		282.532 mm³	

18

English units for rectangular prisms   Name _____

                                              Date _____

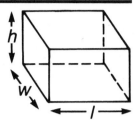

Complete the following.
Use *V = lwh* and *S = 2lw + 2hw + 2hl.*
Be sure to write units in your answers.

	l	*w*	*h*	*V*	*S*
1.	8 yd	2 yd	3 yd	$48yd^3$	$92yd^2$
2.	7 ft	6 ft	4 ft		
3.	46 in.	17 in.	12 in.		
4.	$\frac{7}{8}$ in.	$\frac{3}{4}$ in.	$\frac{5}{16}$ in.		
5.	$3\frac{5}{6}$ yd	$2\frac{1}{4}$ yd	$2\frac{1}{2}$ yd		
6.	$6\frac{2}{3}$ ft	$5\frac{1}{4}$ ft	$1\frac{3}{4}$ ft		
7.	$5\frac{3}{4}$ in.	$3\frac{1}{8}$ in.	$2\frac{1}{2}$ in.		
8.	23 ft	10 ft		1150 ft³	

Metric units for rectangular prisms

Name _____

Date _____

Complete the following.

Use $V = lwh$ and $S = 2lw + 2hw + 2hl$.

Be sure to write units in your answers.

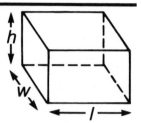

	l	*w*	*h*	*V*	*S*
1.	63 m	22 m	13 m	*18,018 m³*	*4982 m²*
2.	7.2 cm	6.1 cm	3.2 cm		
3.	0.53 m	0.41 m	0.37 m		
4.	5.6 cm	4.7 cm	1.5 cm		
5.	9.2 mm	8.1 mm	5.4 mm		
6.		15 mm	9 mm	2295 mm³	
7.	40 cm		17 cm	21,760 cm³	

20

Volume and surface area of
rectangular prisms

Name _____

Date _____

Solve each of the following.

1. A room in a warehouse is to have all walls painted, including ceiling and floor. One gallon of paint covers 50 square feet. The room measures 80 feet by 60 feet by 20 feet. How many gallons of paint are needed?

    304 gal

2. A hole in a gravel pit measures 200 yards by 150 yards and is 18 yards deep. How many cubic yards of gravel have been removed?

3. How many cubic feet of concrete are needed to pour a patio 30 feet long, 20 feet wide and $\frac{1}{3}$ foot deep?

4. What is the volume of a rectangular can whose measurements are 3 inches by 4 inches by 13 inches?

5. A waterbed has dimensions of 6 feet by 5 feet and is $\frac{2}{3}$ foot deep. One cubic foot of water contains 7.48 gallons. How many gallons of water does the waterbed hold?

More volume and surface area
of rectangular prisms

Name _____

Date _____

Solve each of the following.

1. A trailer measures $7\frac{1}{2}$ feet by 14 feet by $4\frac{2}{3}$ feet. How many cubic feet of sand will the trailer hold?

    490 ft³

2. A rectangular package has dimensions of 20 inches by 15 inches by 12 inches. How many square inches of paper are needed to cover it?

3. A cargo container in the shape of a rectangular prism is to be painted before being loaded onto the cargo ship. Its dimensions are 20 feet by 18 feet by 12 feet. One gallon of paint will cover 204 square feet. How many gallons of paint are need to paint it?

4. A box in the shape of a cube is to be covered with adhesive paper. The box is 30 inches on each edge. How many square inches of paper are needed?

5. A rectangular gasoline tank has dimensions $4\frac{1}{2}$ feet by 3 feet by $\frac{5}{6}$ foot. There are 7.48 gallons in one cubic foot. How many gallons will the tank hold?

Solve each of the following.

1. A room in a warehouse is to have all walls painted, including ceiling and floor. One gallon of paint covers 40 square feet. The room measures 100 feet by 80 feet by 15 feet. How many gallons of paint are needed?

    535 gal

2. A hole in a gravel pit measures 100 yards by 100 yards by 15 yards. How many cubic yards of gravel have been removed?

3. A patio is 40 feet by 20 feet and $\frac{1}{2}$ foot deep. How many cubic feet of concrete are needed to pour the patio?

4. What is the volume of a rectangular can whose dimensions are $2\frac{3}{4}$ inches by $6\frac{2}{3}$ inches by 10 inches?

5. A waterbed is 7 feet long, 5 feet wide and 1 foot deep. One cubic foot contains 7.48 gallons. How many gallons of water does the waterbed hold?

Name _____

Date _____

Solve each of the following.

1. A trailer measures $6\frac{1}{2}$ feet by $10\frac{2}{3}$ feet by $4\frac{1}{2}$ feet. How many cubic feet of sand will the trailer hold?

    $312 \; ft^3$

2. A package is in the shape of a rectangular prism. The dimensions of the package are 25 inches by 12 inches by 8 inches. How many square inches of paper are needed to cover it?

3. A cargo container in the shape of a rectangular prism is to be painted before being loaded onto the cargo ship. Its dimensions are 24 feet by 12 feet by 6 feet. One gallon of paint will cover 252 square feet. How many gallons of paint are needed to paint it?

4. A box in the shape of a cube is to be covered with adhesive paper. The dimensions of the box are 25 inches by 25 inches by 25 inches. How many square inches of paper are needed?

5. A rectangular fuel tank has dimensions 3 feet by $2\frac{1}{2}$ feet by $\frac{2}{3}$ foot. There are 7.48 gallons in one cubic foot. How many gallons will the tank hold?

Volume and surface area of
rectangular prisms

Name _____

Date _____

Solve each of the following.

1. A room in a warehouse is to have all walls painted, including ceiling and floor. One gallon of paint covers 60 square feet. The room measures 90 feet by 80 feet by 18 feet. How many gallons of paint will be needed?

342 gal

2. A hole in a gravel pit measures 150 yards by 100 yards and is 10 yards deep. How many cubic yards of gravel have been removed?

3. A patio is 45 feet by 14 feet by $\frac{1}{4}$ foot. How many cubic feet of concrete are needed to pour the patio?

4. What is the volume of a rectangular-shaped can whose dimensions are $4\frac{1}{2}$ inches by $6\frac{2}{3}$ inches by 11 inches?

5. A waterbed is $6\frac{1}{2}$ feet by 4 feet by $\frac{3}{4}$ foot. One cubic foot contains 7.48 gallons. How many gallons of water does the waterbed hold?

More volume and surface area
of rectangular prisms

Name _____

Date _____

Solve each of the following.

1. A trailer measures $4\frac{2}{3}$ feet by $6\frac{3}{4}$ feet by 7 feet. How many cubic feet of sand will the trailer hold?

$220\frac{1}{2} ft^3$

2. A package is in the shape of a rectangular prism. The dimensions of the package are 28 inches by 20 inches by 15 inches. How many square inches of paper are needed to cover it?

3. A cargo container in the shape of a rectangular prism is to be painted before being loaded onto the cargo ship. Its dimensions are 18 feet by 14 feet by 10 feet. One gallon of paint will cover 143 square feet. How many gallons of paint are needed to paint it?

4. A box in the shape of a cube is to be covered with adhesive paper. The dimensions of the box are 20 inches by 20 inches by 20 inches. How many square inches of paper are needed?

5. A rectangular fuel tank has dimensions $2\frac{1}{2}$ feet by 2 feet by $\frac{3}{4}$ foot. There are 7.48 gallons in one cubic foot. How many gallons will the tank hold?

26

Volume and surface area of
rectangular prisms

Name _____

Date _____

Solve each of the following.

1. A room in a warehouse is to have all walls painted, including ceiling and floor. One gallon of paint covers 80 square feet. The room measures 90 feet by 90 feet by 20 feet. How many gallons of paint will be needed?

$292\frac{1}{2}$ gal

2. A hole in a gravel pit measures 180 yards by 125 yards and is 12 yards deep. How many cubic yards of gravel have been removed?

3. A patio is 50 feet by 30 feet by $\frac{1}{3}$ foot deep. How many cubic feet of concrete are needed to pour the patio?

4. What is the volume of a rectangular-shaped can whose dimensions are $5\frac{1}{2}$ inches by $5\frac{1}{3}$ inches by 11 inches?

5. A waterbed is 5 feet by $4\frac{1}{2}$ feet by $\frac{2}{3}$ foot. One cubic foot holds 7.48 gallons. How many gallons of water does the waterbed hold?

More volume and surface area
of rectangular prisms

Name _____

Date _____

Solve each of the following.

1. A trailer measures $7\frac{1}{2}$ feet by $4\frac{1}{3}$ feet by 10 feet. How many cubic feet of sand will the trailer hold?

   $325\ ft^3$

2. A package is in the shape of a rectangular prism. The dimensions of the package are 18 inches by 15 inches by 10 inches. How many square inches of paper are needed to cover it?

3. A cargo container in the shape of a rectangular prism is to be painted before being loaded onto the cargo ship. Its dimensions are 30 feet by 20 feet by 15 feet. One gallon of paint will cover 300 square feet. How many gallons of paint are needed to paint it?

4. A box in the shape of a cube is to be covered with adhesive paper. The dimensions of the box are 18 inches by 18 inches by 18 inches. How many square inches of paper are needed?

5. A rectangular fuel tank has dimensions 2 feet by $1\frac{1}{2}$ feet by $\frac{1}{2}$ foot. There are 7.48 gallons in one cubic foot. How many gallons will the tank hold?

28

Volume and surface area of
rectangular prisms

Solve each of the following.

1. A room in a warehouse is to have all walls painted, including ceiling and floor. One gallon of paint covers 70 square feet. The room measures 120 feet by 100 feet by 25 feet. How many gallons of paint will be needed?

   500 gal

2. A hole in a gravel pit measures 140 yards by 95 yards by 9 yards. How many cubic yards of gravel have been removed?

3. A patio is 25 feet by 15 feet by $\frac{1}{3}$ foot deep. How many cubic feet of concrete are needed to pour the patio?

4. What is the volume of a rectangular-shaped can whose dimensions are $7\frac{1}{2}$ inches by $4\frac{2}{3}$ inches by 13 inches?

5. A waterbed is 7 feet by 6 feet by $\frac{5}{6}$ foot. One cubic foot holds 7.48 gallons. How many gallons of water does the waterbed hold?

More volume and surface area
of rectangular prisms

Name _____

Date _____

Solve each of the following.

1. A trailer measures $8\frac{2}{3}$ feet by $6\frac{1}{2}$ feet by 7 feet. How many cubic feet of sand will the trailer hold?

$394\frac{1}{3} ft^3$

2. A package is in the shape of a rectangular prism. The dimensions of the package are 26 inches by 20 inches by 18 inches. How many square inches of paper are needed to cover it?

3. A cargo container in the shape of a rectangular prism is to be painted before being loaded onto the cargo ship. Its dimensions are 24 feet by 16 feet by 10 feet. One gallon of paint will cover 392 square feet. How many gallons of paint are needed to paint it?

4. A box in the shape of a cube is to be covered with adhesive paper. The dimensions of the box are 12 inches by 12 inches by 12 inches. How many square inches of paper are needed?

5. A rectangular fuel tank has dimensions 3 feet by $1\frac{1}{2}$ feet by $\frac{2}{3}$ foot. There are 7.48 gallons in one cubic foot. How many gallons will the tank hold?

English units for triangular prisms and pyramids

Name _____

Date _____

Complete the following for triangular prisms.

Use $V = \frac{1}{2}abh$.

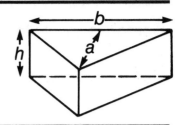

	a	b	h	V
1.	7 ft	12 ft	4 ft	*168 ft³*
2.	21 in.	16 in.	5 in.	
3.	$5\frac{1}{3}$ yd	$1\frac{1}{2}$ yd	$2\frac{2}{3}$ yd	
4.	$3\frac{1}{2}$ ft	$2\frac{1}{4}$ ft	$1\frac{1}{3}$ ft	
5.	8 in.	15 in.		660 in.³
6.	7 in.	13 in.		910 in.³

Complete the following for triangular pyramids.

Use $V = \frac{1}{6}abh$.

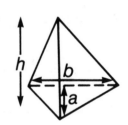

	a	b	h	V
7.	15 ft	12 ft	5 ft	
8.	16 in.	24 in.	9 in.	
9.	$4\frac{2}{3}$ ft	$2\frac{1}{4}$ ft	2 ft	
10.	$3\frac{1}{2}$ yd	$2\frac{2}{3}$ yd	$2\frac{1}{4}$ yd	
11.	8 ft	4 ft		32 ft³
12.		3 in.	8 in.	28 in.³

Metric units for triangular
prisms and pyramids

Name _____

Date _____

Complete the following for triangular prisms.

Use $V = \frac{1}{2}abh$.

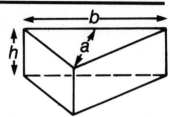

	a	b	h	V
1.	15 mm	8 mm	3 mm	$180\,mm^3$
2.	3.5 cm	2.1 cm	1.4 cm	
3.	2.4 m	1.3 m	0.8 m	
4.	12 cm	18 cm		1620 cm³

Complete the following for triangular pyramids.

Use $V = \frac{1}{6}abh$.

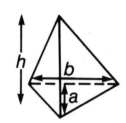

	a	b	h	V
5.	13 m	11 m	12 m	
6.	2.4 cm	3.1 cm	1.2 cm	
7.	6.3 m	2.2 m	3 m	
8.	12 cm		3 cm	30 cm³

English units for triangular
prisms and pyramids

Name _____

Date _____

Complete the following for triangular prisms.

Use $V = \frac{1}{2}abh$.

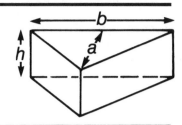

	a	b	h	V
1.	9 yd	13 yd	6 yd	351 yd³
2.	22 in.	7 in.	5 in.	
3.	$3\frac{1}{4}$ ft	$5\frac{1}{3}$ ft	$2\frac{1}{2}$ ft	
4.	$2\frac{2}{3}$ yd	$4\frac{1}{2}$ yd	$2\frac{1}{3}$ yd	
5.	16 ft	7 ft		616 ft³
6.	11 in.		16 in.	1144 in.³

Complete the following for triangular pyramids.

Use $V = \frac{1}{6}abh$.

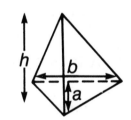

	a	b	h	V
7.	18 in.	13 in.	7 in.	
8.	19 ft	16 ft	9 ft	
9.	$8\frac{2}{3}$ ft	$4\frac{1}{4}$ ft	$1\frac{1}{3}$ ft	
10.	$5\frac{1}{4}$ yd	$3\frac{2}{3}$ yd	$1\frac{1}{3}$ yd	
11.	13 in.		12 in.	130 in.³
12.		3 ft	7 ft	28 ft³

Complete the following for triangular prisms.

Use $V = \frac{1}{2}abh$.

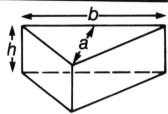

	a	b	h	V
1.	17 cm	14 cm	8 cm	952 cm³
2.	6.7 mm	2.8 mm	3.1 mm	
3.	1.8 cm	3.4 cm	2.3 cm	
4.		13 cm	9 cm	1287 cm³

Complete the following for triangular pyramids.

Use $V = \frac{1}{6}abh$.

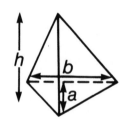

	a	b	h	V
5.	13 m	7 m	12 m	
6.	6.1 cm	2.1 cm	4 cm	
7.	5.4 cm	7.2 cm	4.1 cm	
8.	4 cm	9 cm		78 cm³

34

English units for triangular
prisms and pyramids

Name _____

Date _____

Complete the following for triangular prisms.

Use $V = \frac{1}{2}abh$.

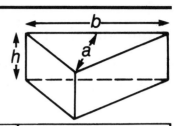

	a	b	h	V
1.	28 in.	6 in.	9 in.	756 in.³
2.	5 ft	14 ft	7 ft	
3.	$3\frac{1}{4}$ yd	$3\frac{1}{3}$ yd	$1\frac{1}{2}$ yd	
4.	$2\frac{3}{4}$ ft	$3\frac{1}{4}$ ft	$2\frac{2}{3}$ ft	
5.	14 in.	16 in.		560 in.³

Complete the following for triangular pyramids.

Use $V = \frac{1}{6}abh$.

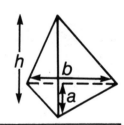

	a	b	h	V
6.	21 ft	16 ft	10 ft	
7.	19 in.	12 in.	8 in.	
8.	$4\frac{1}{8}$ in.	$2\frac{1}{4}$ in.	4 in.	
9.	$6\frac{1}{2}$ ft	$4\frac{2}{3}$ ft	$3\frac{1}{3}$ ft	
10.		12 in.	9 in.	234 in.³

Metric units for triangular
prisms and pyramids

Name _____

Date _____

Complete the following for triangular prisms.

Use $V = \frac{1}{2}abh$.

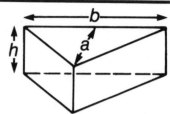

	a	b	h	V
1.	15 mm	9 mm	10 mm	675 mm²
2.	5.6 m	7.2 m	0.6 m	
3.	6.5 cm	8.1 cm	4.2 cm	
4.	21 mm		23 mm	3381 mm³
5.		22 cm	14 cm	1078 cm³

Complete the following for triangular pyramids.

Use $V = \frac{1}{6}abh$.

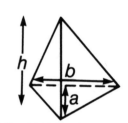

	a	b	h	V
6.	17 cm	16 cm	9 cm	
7.	3.9 cm	4.3 cm	2 cm	
8.	6.3 m	5.1 m	2.4 m	
9.	15 mm	4 mm		50 mm³
10.	21 cm		11 cm	1001 cm³

English units for triangular
prisms and pyramids

Name _____

Date _____

Complete the following for triangular prisms.

Use $V = \frac{1}{2}abh$.

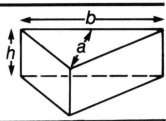

	a	b	h	V
1.	6 yd	15 yd	9 yd	405 yd³
2.	11 in.	16 in.	3 in.	
3.	$4\frac{1}{2}$ ft	$3\frac{1}{3}$ ft	$2\frac{1}{2}$ ft	
4.	$1\frac{1}{3}$ yd	$2\frac{1}{4}$ yd	$2\frac{1}{3}$ yd	
5.	26 in.		11 in.	1287 in.³
6.	14 ft	20 ft		980 ft³

Complete the following for triangular pyramids.

Use $V = \frac{1}{6}abh$.

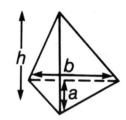

	a	b	h	V
7.	25 in.	14 in.	21 in.	
8.	13 ft	12 ft	8 ft	
9.	$5\frac{1}{2}$ in.	$6\frac{3}{4}$ in.	10 in.	
10.	$3\frac{2}{3}$ yd	$2\frac{1}{4}$ yd	$4\frac{2}{3}$ yd	
11.	14 in.	33 in.		539 in.³

37

Metric units for triangular
prisms and pyramids

Name _____

Date _____

Complete the following for triangular prisms.

Use $V = \frac{1}{2}abh$.

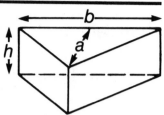

	a	b	h	V
1.	13 cm	17 cm	12 cm	1326 cm³
2.	8.3 mm	4.2 mm	3.4 mm	
3.	3.5 m	4.1 m	5.2 m	
4.		13 m	11 m	1001 m³

Complete the following for triangular pyramids.

Use $V = \frac{1}{6}abh$.

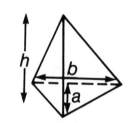

	a	b	h	V
5.	17 cm	15 cm	10 cm	
6.	7.3 cm	5.1 cm	6 cm	
7.	4.6 mm	3.9 mm	5.1 mm	
8.		5 cm	23 cm	345 cm³
9.	22 mm		21 mm	1463 mm³

English units for triangular
prisms and pyramids

Name _____

Date _____

Complete the following for triangular prisms.

Use $V = \frac{1}{2}abh$.

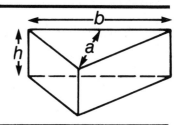

	a	b	h	V
1.	8 ft	18 ft	5 ft	360 ft³
2.	12 in.	9 in.	13 in.	
3.	$2\frac{2}{3}$ yd	$3\frac{1}{4}$ yd	$1\frac{1}{4}$ yd	
4.	$4\frac{3}{4}$ ft	$1\frac{1}{3}$ ft	$4\frac{1}{4}$ ft	
5.	21 in.		13 in.	1638 in.³
6.	14 ft	18 ft		378 ft³

Complete the following for triangular pyramids.

Use $V = \frac{1}{6}abh$.

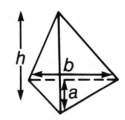

	a	b	h	V
7.	25 ft	14 ft	6 ft	
8.	23 ft	9 ft	8 ft	
9.	$5\frac{1}{2}$ in.	$6\frac{3}{4}$ in.	2 in.	
10.	$2\frac{2}{3}$ yd	$4\frac{1}{6}$ yd	$3\frac{3}{4}$ yd	
11.	31 in.		22 in.	1705 in.³
12.	51 ft	16 ft		5712 ft³

Metric units for triangular
prisms and pyramids

Name _____

Date _____

Complete the following for triangular prisms.

Use $V = \frac{1}{2}abh$.

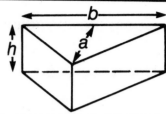

	a	b	h	V
1.	14 mm	19 mm	7 mm	$931\ mm^3$
2.	2.1 m	3.9 m	0.6 m	
3.	6.7 cm	8.1 cm	0.8 cm	
4.		15 m	18 m	2160 m³

Complete the following for triangular pyramids.

Use $V = \frac{1}{6}abh$.

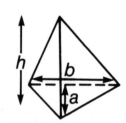

	a	b	h	V
5.	14 cm	6 cm	13 cm	
6.	7.2 m	5.2 m	4 m	
7.	3.9 cm	6.2 cm	3.1 cm	
8.		28 cm	33 cm	6622 cm³

Measuring circles

Use a flexible ruler to measure the circumference and diameter of each circle to the nearest millimeter. Next write the ratio of circumference to diameter first as a fraction, and then as a decimal to the nearest hundredth.

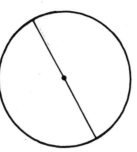

circumference = 113 mm

diameter = 36 mm

$$\frac{\text{circumference}}{\text{diameter}} = \frac{113}{36}$$

$$= 3.14$$

1. circumference = _____

diameter = _____

$$\frac{\text{circumference}}{\text{diameter}} = \underline{\quad}$$

$$= \underline{\quad}$$

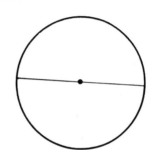

2. circumference = _____

diameter = _____

$$\frac{\text{circumference}}{\text{diameter}} = \underline{\quad}$$

$$= \underline{\quad}$$

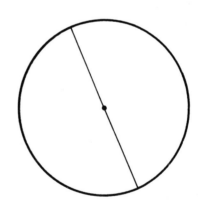

3. circumference = _____

diameter = _____

$$\frac{\text{circumference}}{\text{diameter}} = \underline{\quad}$$

$$= \underline{\quad}$$

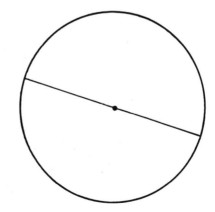

More measuring circles

Name _____

Date _____

Suppose the diameter of a circle is 36 mm. Then, the radius, circumference and area can be found as follows, using 3.14 for π.

$$r = \tfrac{1}{2}d \qquad\qquad C = \pi d \qquad\qquad A = \pi r^2$$
$$ = \tfrac{1}{2}(36) \qquad\quad\ = (3.14)(36) \qquad\ = (3.14)(18^2)$$
$$ = 18 \text{ mm} \qquad\quad = 113.04 \text{ mm} \qquad = 1017.36 \text{ mm}^2$$

Measure the diameter of each circle to the nearest millimeter. Then find r, C, and A. Use 3.14 for π.

1. $d =$ _____
   $r =$ _____
   $C =$ _____
   $A =$ _____

2. $d =$ _____
   $r =$ _____
   $C =$ _____
   $A =$ _____

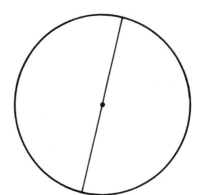

3. $d =$ _____
   $r =$ _____
   $C =$ _____
   $A =$ _____

Measuring circles

Use a flexible ruler to measure the circumference and diameter of each circle to the nearest millimeter. Next write the ratio of circumference to diameter first as a fraction, and then as a decimal to the nearest hundredth.

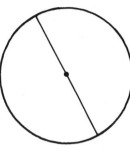

circumference = 113 mm

diameter = 36 mm

$$\frac{circumference}{diameter} = \frac{113}{36}$$

$$= 3.14$$

1. circumference = _____

diameter = _____

$\dfrac{circumference}{diameter}$ = _____

= _____

2. circumference = _____

diameter = _____

$\dfrac{circumference}{diameter}$ = _____

= _____

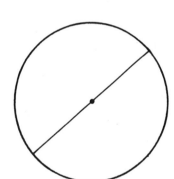

3. circumference = _____

diameter = _____

$\dfrac{circumference}{diameter}$ = _____

= _____

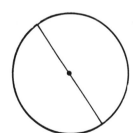

Suppose the diameter of a circle is 36 mm. Then, the radius, circumference and area can be found as follows, using 3.14 for π.

$$r = \tfrac{1}{2}d$$
$$= \tfrac{1}{2}(36)$$
$$= 18 \text{ mm}$$

$$C = \pi d$$
$$= (3.14)(36)$$
$$= 113.04 \text{ mm}$$

$$A = \pi r^2$$
$$= (3.14)(18^2)$$
$$= 1017.36 \text{ mm}^2$$

Measure the diameter of each circle to the nearest millimeter. Then find r, C, and A. Use 3.14 for π.

1. $d = $ _____
   $r = $ _____
   $C = $ _____
   $A = $ _____

2. $d = $ _____
   $r = $ _____
   $C = $ _____
   $A = $ _____

3. $d = $ _____
   $r = $ _____
   $C = $ _____
   $A = $ _____

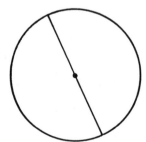

Measuring circles

Use a flexible ruler to measure the circumference and diameter of each circle to the nearest millimeter. Next write the ratio of circumference to diameter first as a fraction, and then as a decimal to the nearest hundredth.

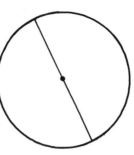

circumference = 113 mm

diameter   = 36 mm

$$\frac{circumference}{diameter} = \frac{113}{36}$$

$$= 3.14$$

1. circumference = _____

diameter = _____

$$\frac{circumference}{diameter} = \text{_____}$$

$$= \text{_____}$$

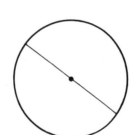

2. circumference = _____

diameter = _____

$$\frac{circumference}{diameter} = \text{_____}$$

$$= \text{_____}$$

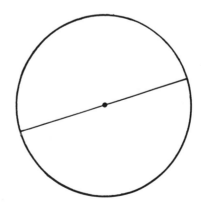

3. circumference = _____

diameter = _____

$$\frac{circumference}{diameter} = \text{_____}$$

$$= \text{_____}$$

Name _____

Date _____

Suppose the diameter of a circle is 36 mm. Then, the radius, circumference and area can be found as follows, using 3.14 for π.

$$r = \tfrac{1}{2}d$$
$$= \tfrac{1}{2}(36)$$
$$= 18 \text{ mm}$$

$$C = \pi d$$
$$= (3.14)(36)$$
$$= 113.04 \text{ mm}$$

$$A = \pi r^2$$
$$= (3.14)(18^2)$$
$$= 1017.36 \text{ mm}^2$$

Measure the diameter of each circle to the nearest millimeter. Then find r, C, and A. Use 3.14 for π.

1. $d =$ _____
  $r =$ _____
  $C =$ _____
  $A =$ _____

2. $d =$ _____
  $r =$ _____
  $C =$ _____
  $A =$ _____

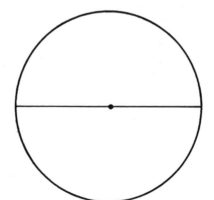

3. $d =$ _____
  $r =$ _____
  $C =$ _____
  $A =$ _____

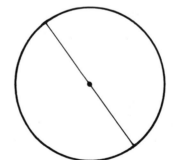

Measuring circles

Name _____

Date _____

Use a flexible ruler to measure the circumference and diameter of each circle to the nearest millimeter. Next write the ratio of circumference to diameter first as a fraction, and then as a decimal to the nearest hundredth.

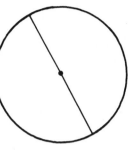

$$\text{circumference} = 113 \text{ mm}$$
$$\text{diameter} = 36 \text{ mm}$$
$$\frac{\text{circumference}}{\text{diameter}} = \frac{113}{36}$$
$$= 3.14$$

1. circumference = _____

diameter = _____

$\dfrac{\text{circumference}}{\text{diameter}}$ = _____

= _____

2. circumference = _____

diameter = _____

$\dfrac{\text{circumference}}{\text{diameter}}$ = _____

= _____

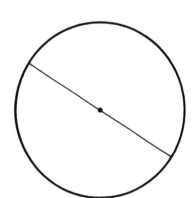

3. circumference = _____

diameter = _____

$\dfrac{\text{circumference}}{\text{diameter}}$ = _____

= _____

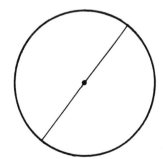

Name _____

Date _____

Suppose the diameter of a circle is 36 mm. Then, the radius, circumference and area can be found as follows, using 3.14 for π.

$$r = \tfrac{1}{2}d$$
$$= \tfrac{1}{2}(36)$$
$$= 18 \text{ mm}$$

$$C = \pi d$$
$$= (3.14)(36)$$
$$= 113.04 \text{ mm}$$

$$A = \pi r^2$$
$$= (3.14)(18^2)$$
$$= 1017.36 \text{ mm}^2$$

Measure the diameter of each circle to the nearest millimeter. Then find r, C, and A. Use 3.14 for π.

1. $d =$ _____
   $r =$ _____
   $C =$ _____
   $A =$ _____

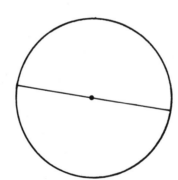

2. $d =$ _____
   $r =$ _____
   $C =$ _____
   $A =$ _____

3. $d =$ _____
   $r =$ _____
   $C =$ _____
   $A =$ _____

Measuring circles

Use a flexible ruler to measure
the circumference and diameter
of each circle to the nearest
millimeter. Next write the ratio of
circumference to diameter first
as a fraction, and then as a decimal
to the nearest hundredth.

circumference = 113 mm

diameter = 36 mm

$$\frac{circumference}{diameter} = \frac{113}{36}$$

$$= 3.14$$

1. circumference = _____

    diameter = _____

$$\frac{circumference}{diameter} = \underline{\quad}$$

$$= \underline{\quad}$$

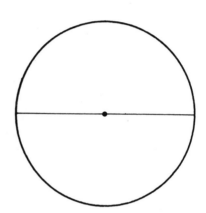

2. circumference = _____

    diameter = _____

$$\frac{circumference}{diameter} = \underline{\quad}$$

$$= \underline{\quad}$$

3. circumference = _____

    diameter = _____

$$\frac{circumference}{diameter} = \underline{\quad}$$

$$= \underline{\quad}$$

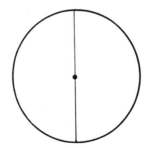

More measuring circles

Name _____

Date _____

Suppose the diameter of a circle is 36 mm. Then, the radius, circumference and area can be found as follows, using 3.14 for π.

$r = \frac{1}{2}d$ $C = \pi d$ $A = \pi r^2$

$\quad = \frac{1}{2}(36)$ $\quad = (3.14)(36)$ $\quad = (3.14)(18^2)$

$\quad = 18$ mm $\quad = 113.04$ mm $\quad = 1017.36$ mm²

Measure the diameter of each circle to the nearest millimeter. Then find r, C, and A. Use 3.14 for π.

1. $d =$ _____

$\quad r =$ _____

$\quad C =$ _____

$\quad A =$ _____

2. $d =$ _____

$\quad r =$ _____

$\quad C =$ _____

$\quad A =$ _____

3. $d =$ _____

$\quad r =$ _____

$\quad C =$ _____

$\quad A =$ _____

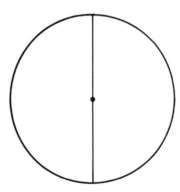

Circumference and area of circles

Name _____

Date _____

Complete the following. Use $\frac{22}{7}$ for π.

	radius	diameter	circumference $C = \pi d$	area $A = \pi r^2$
1.	21	42	132	1386
2.	63			
3.	$5\frac{8}{11}$			
4.	$3\frac{2}{11}$			
5.	$8\frac{3}{11}$			

Complete the following. Use 3.14 for π.

	radius	diameter	circumference $C = \pi d$	area $A = \pi r^2$
6.		30		
7.		8.2		
8.		12.4		
9.		7		
10.		0.74		

Aldo's Pizza

	10" Small	12" Medium	14" Large	16" Ex. Large	24" Family	30" Party
ALDO'S COMBINATION	3.15	4.45	5.80	6.70	10.45	16.00
Cheese — Salami — Pepperoni — Olives — Mushrooms — Sausage						
ALDO'S SPECIAL	3.50	5.00	6.45	7.45	10.60	17.45
Same as Combo plus Green Peppers and Onions						
ALDO'S SUPREME	3.90	5.50	7.15	8.20	12.55	18.85
Same as Special plus Tomatoes — Extra Cheese on Top						
ALDO'S VEGETARIAN	3.15	4.45	5.80	6.70	10.45	16.00
Cheese — Tomatoes — Green Peppers — Onions — Mushrooms — Olives						

Suppose you are going to buy Aldo's *Combination Pizza.*
You have $20 to spend.

1. How many small (10" diam.) pizzas can you buy? __6__
2. How much change will you receive? _____

3. How many party (30" diam.) pizzas can you buy? _____
4. How much change you will receive? _____

5. Which will give you more square inches of pizza to eat, six small pizzas or one party pizza? _____

   six small pizzas

   $A = \pi r^2 \times 6$
   $\quad = 3.14 \times \underline{\hspace{1cm}} \times 6$
   $\quad = \underline{\hspace{1cm}} \times 6$
   $\quad = \underline{\hspace{1cm}}$

   one party pizza

   $A = \pi r^2$
   $\quad = 3.14 \times \underline{\hspace{1cm}}$
   $\quad = \underline{\hspace{1cm}}$

Circumference and area of circles

Name _____

Date _____

Complete the following. Use $\frac{22}{7}$ for π.

	radius	diameter	circumference $C = \pi d$	area $A = \pi r^2$
1.	11	22	$69\frac{1}{7}$	$380\frac{2}{7}$
2.		44		
3.		$10\frac{2}{11}$		
4.		$18\frac{2}{3}$		
5.		$12\frac{4}{9}$		

Complete the following. Use 3.14 for π.

	radius	diameter	circumference $C = \pi d$	area $A = \pi r^2$
6.	28			
7.	26			
8.	6.3			
9.	8.2			
10.	0.43			

Name _____

Date _____

Aldo's Pizza

	10" Small	12" Medium	14" Large	16" Ex. Large	24" Family	30" Party
ALDO'S COMBINATION	3.15	4.45	5.80	6.70	10.45	16.00
Cheese — Salami — Pepperoni — Olives — Mushrooms — Sausage						
ALDO'S SPECIAL	3.50	5.00	6.45	7.45	10.60	17.45
Same as Combo plus Green Peppers and Onions						
ALDO'S SUPREME	3.90	5.50	7.15	8.20	12.55	18.85
Same as Special plus Tomatoes — Extra Cheese on Top						
ALDO'S VEGETARIAN	3.15	4.45	5.80	6.70	10.45	16.00
Cheese — Tomatoes — Green Peppers — Onions — Mushrooms — Olives						

Solve each problem about Aldo's *Special Pizza.*

1. Find the area of one small (10" diam.) pizza.

   $A = \pi r^2$
   $= 3.14 \times \underline{25\ in.^2}$
   $= \underline{78.5\ in.^2}$

2. Find the area of one family (24" diam.) pizza.

   $A = \pi r^2$
   $= 3.14 \times \underline{\hspace{1cm}}$
   $= \underline{\hspace{1cm}}$

3. Suppose a small pizza is about right for one person. How many people can eat a family pizza? _____

4. Suppose the number of people in problem **3** buy a family pizza rather than small pizzas for each. How much money do they save? _____

5. Is the savings worthwhile? _____

54

Circumference and area of circles

Name _____

Date _____

Complete the following. Use $\frac{22}{7}$ for π.

	radius	diameter	circumference $C = \pi d$	area $A = \pi r^2$
1.	14	28	88	616
2.		84		
3.	$5\frac{1}{4}$			
4.	$6\frac{3}{4}$			
5.	$12\frac{3}{5}$			

Complete the following. Use 3.14 for π.

	radius	diameter	circumference $C = \pi d$	area $A = \pi r^2$
6.	49			
7.		8.4		
8.		11.2		
9.	8.9			
10.	7.6			

Using circles

Name _____

Date _____

Aldo's Pizza

	10" Small	12" Medium	14" Large	16" Ex. Large	24" Family	30" Party
ALDO'S COMBINATION	3.15	4.45	5.80	6.70	10.45	16.00
Cheese — Salami — Pepperoni — Olives — Mushrooms — Sausage						
ALDO'S SPECIAL	3.50	5.00	6.45	7.45	10.60	17.45
Same as Combo plus Green Peppers and Onions						
ALDO'S SUPREME	3.90	5.50	7.15	8.20	12.55	18.85
Same as Special plus Tomatoes — Extra Cheese on Top						
ALDO'S VEGETARIAN	3.15	4.45	5.80	6.70	10.45	16.00
Cheese — Tomatoes — Green Peppers — Onions — Mushrooms — Olives						

Solve each problem about Aldo's *Supreme Pizza.*

1. Find the area of one large (14" diam.) pizza.

   $A = \pi r^2$
   $= 3.14 \times \underline{49 \text{ in.}^2}$
   $= \underline{153.86 \text{ in.}^2}$

2. Find the area of one extra large (24" diam.) pizza.

   $A = \pi r^2$
   $= 3.14 \times \underline{\hspace{1.5cm}}$
   $= \underline{\hspace{1.5cm}}$

3. Joe and Dino share a large pizza equally.
   How many square inches does each get? _____

4. How much does each person pay if they share the cost equally? _____

5. Lita, Megan, and Mike share an extra large pizza equally.
   How many square inches does each get? _____

6. How much does each person pay if they share the cost equally? _____

7. Who gets a better deal, Joe and Dino or Lita, Megan, and Mike?

   _____

Circumference and area of circles

Complete the following. Use $\frac{22}{7}$ for π.

	radius	diameter	circumference $C = \pi d$	area $A = \pi r^2$
1.	5	10	$31\frac{3}{7}$	$78\frac{4}{7}$
2.		8		
3.	$5\frac{1}{5}$			
4.	$5\frac{1}{4}$			
5.	$2\frac{5}{8}$			

Complete the following. Use 3.14 for π.

	radius	diameter	circumference $C = \pi d$	area $A = \pi r^2$
6.	3			
7.	17			
8.		8.4		
9.		3		
10.		7.2		

Name _____

Date _____

Aldo's Pizza

	10" Small	12" Medium	14" Large	16" Ex. Large	24" Family	30" Party
ALDO'S COMBINATION	3.15	4.45	5.80	6.70	10.45	16.00
Cheese — Salami — Pepperoni — Olives — Mushrooms — Sausage						
ALDO'S SPECIAL	3.50	5.00	6.45	7.45	10.60	17.45
Same as Combo plus Green Peppers and Onions						
ALDO'S SUPREME	3.90	5.50	7.15	8.20	12.55	18.85
Same as Special plus Tomatoes — Extra Cheese on Top						
ALDO'S VEGETARIAN	3.15	4.45	5.80	6.70	10.45	16.00
Cheese — Tomatoes — Green Peppers — Onions — Mushrooms — Olives						

Solve each problem about pizza.

1. Find the area of one small (10" diam.) pizza.

$A = \pi r^2$

$= 3.14 \times \underline{25 \text{ in.}^2}$

$= \underline{78.5 \text{ in.}^2}$

2. Find the area of one party (30" diam.) pizza.

$A = \pi r^2$

$= 3.14 \times \underline{\hspace{1cm}}$

$= \underline{\hspace{1cm}}$

3. Joan is planning a pizza party. She figures that each person, including herself, 15 friends and 2 adults, can eat one small pizza apiece. How many party pizzas should she order? _____

4. Suppose Joan orders Aldo's *Supreme Pizza* for her party in problem **3.** How much will the pizza cost? _____

58

Circumference and area of circles

Name _____

Date _____

Complete the following. Use $\frac{22}{7}$ for π.

	radius	diameter	circumference $C = \pi d$	area $A = \pi r^2$
1.	7	14	44	154
2.		28		
3.	$\frac{7}{11}$			
4.	$10\frac{1}{2}$			
5.	$5\frac{1}{11}$			

Complete the following. Use 3.14 for π.

	radius	diameter	circumference $C = \pi d$	area $A = \pi r^2$
6.	5			
7.	9			
8.		22		
9.		32		
10.		8.4		

Name _____

Date _____

Aldo's Pizza

	10" Small	12" Medium	14" Large	16" Ex. Large	24" Family	30" Party
ALDO'S COMBINATION	3.15	4.45	5.80	6.70	10.45	16.00
Cheese — Salami — Pepperoni — Olives — Mushrooms — Sausage						
ALDO'S SPECIAL	3.50	5.00	6.45	7.45	10.60	17.45
Same as Combo plus Green Peppers and Onions						
ALDO'S SUPREME	3.90	5.50	7.15	8.20	12.55	18.85
Same as Special plus Tomatoes — Extra Cheese on Top						
ALDO'S VEGETARIAN	3.15	4.45	5.80	6.70	10.45	16.00
Cheese — Tomatoes — Green Peppers — Onions — Mushrooms — Olives						

Solve each problem about pizza.

1. Find the area of one small (10" diam.) pizza. _78.5 in.²_	2. Find the area of one medium (12" diam.) pizza. _____
3. Find the area of one family (24" diam.) pizza. _____	4. Find the area of one party (30" diam.) pizza. _____
5. The area of a family pizza is _____ times the area of a medium pizza.	6. The area of a party pizza is _____ times the area of a small pizza.

Volume and surface area of cylinders

If r is the radius of the base and h is the height of a cylinder, then

$$V = \pi r^2 h$$

where V is the volume.

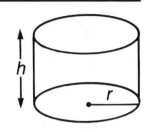

Find the volume of each cylinder given the following. Use 3.14 for π.

	r	h	V
1.	5 cm	12 cm	$942 \, cm^3$
2.	7 mm	10 mm	
3.	12 m	17 m	
4.	20 cm	25 cm	
5.	1.5 dm	8.2 dm	

The surface area of a cylinder is the sum of the areas of a rectangle and two circles.

$$S = 2\pi r^2 + 2\pi rh$$

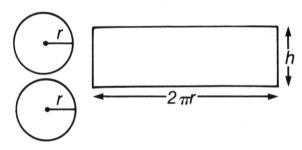

Find the surface area of each cylinder given the following. Use 3.14 for π.

	r	h	S
6.	6 m	9 m	
7.	11 cm	15 cm	
8.	4 dm	6 dm	
9.	30 cm	50 cm	
10.	16 mm	21 mm	

Volume of cones and spheres

Name _____

Date _____

If r is the radius of the base of a cone and h is the height, then

$V = \frac{1}{3}\pi r^2 h$ where V is the volume.

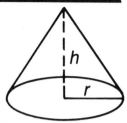

Find the volume of each cone given the following. Use 3.14 for π.

	r	h	V
1.	12 mm	14 mm	$2110.08\ mm^3$
2.	15 cm	18 cm	
3.	21 dm	26 dm	
4.	9 m	12 m	
5.	6 cm	20 cm	

If r is the radius of a sphere, then

$$V = \frac{4}{3}\pi r^3$$

where V is the volume.

Find the volume of each sphere given the following. Use 3.14 for π.

	r	V
6.	9 m	
7.	15 cm	
8.	3 cm	
9.	6 dm	
10.	12 mm	
11.	1.5 m	

Volume and surface area of cylinders

If r is the radius of the base and h is the height of a cylinder, then

$$V = \pi r^2 h$$

where V is the volume.

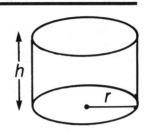

Find the volume of each cylinder given the following. Use 3.14 for π.

	r	h	V
1.	1.1 cm	2.5 cm	9.4985 cm³
2.	2 m	12 m	
3.	2.4 dm	5 dm	
4.	3 m	7 m	
5.	5 mm	13 mm	

The surface area of a cylinder is the sum of the areas of a rectangle and two circles.

$$S = 2\pi r^2 + 2\pi rh$$

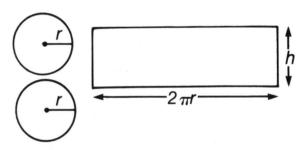

Find the surface area of each cylinder given the following. Use 3.14 for π.

	r	h	S
6.	7 mm	10 mm	
7.	8 dm	14 dm	
8.	2.3 dkm	6 dkm	
9.	1.8 m	2.4 m	
10.	10 cm	20 cm	

63

Volume of cones and spheres

Name _____
Date _____

If *r* is the radius of the base of a
cone and *h* is the height, then

$V = \frac{1}{3}\pi r^2 h$ where *V* is the volume.

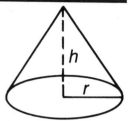

Find the volume of each cone given the following. Use 3.14 for π.

	r	h	V
1.	15 mm	19 mm	4474.5 mm³
2.	3 m	8 m	
3.	6 cm	20 cm	
4.	1.5 dm	8.1 dm	
5.	16 cm	18 cm	

If *r* is the radius of a sphere, then

$$V = \frac{4}{3}\pi r^3$$

where *V* is the volume.

Find the volume of each sphere given the following. Use 3.14 for π.

	r	V
6.	1.5 cm	
7.	2.1 m	
8.	12 dm	
9.	2.4 cm	
10.	6 mm	
11.	3 cm	

Volume and surface area of cylinders   Name _____

Date _____

If r is the radius of the base and h is the height of a cylinder, then

$$V = \pi r^2 h$$

where V is the volume.

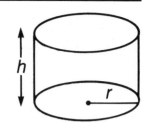

Find the volume of each cylinder given the following. Use 3.14 for π.

	r	h	V
1.	17 dkm	20 dkm	18,149.2 dkm³
2.	12.1 cm	4 cm	
3.	0.86 mm	2 mm	
4.	0.4 m	0.5 m	
5.	10 cm	12 cm	

The surface area of a cylinder is the sum of the areas of a rectangle and two circles.

$$S = 2\pi r^2 + 2\pi rh$$

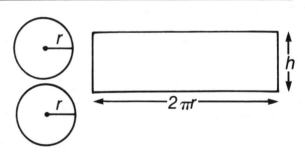

Find the surface area of each cylinder given the following. Use 3.14 for π.

	r	h	S
6.	4 m	9 m	
7.	7 dm	10 dm	
8.	3 cm	4 cm	
9.	0.15 mm	0.25 mm	
10.	40 m	50 m	

65

Volume of cones and spheres

Name _____

Date _____

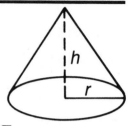

If r is the radius of the base of a cone and h is the height, then

$V = \frac{1}{3}\pi r^2 h$ where V is the volume.

Find the volume of each cone given the following. Use 3.14 for π.

	r	h	V
1.	21 cm	25 cm	11,539.5 cm³
2.	6 dm	11 dm	
3.	9 cm	16 cm	
4.	12 mm	26 mm	
5.	4 m	21 m	

If r is the radius of a sphere, then

$$V = \frac{4}{3}\pi r^3$$

where V is the volume.

Find the volume of each sphere given the following. Use 3.14 for π.

	r	V
6.	1.8 dm	
7.	8.1 cm	
8.	0.15 m	
9.	2.7 cm	
10.	0.24 m	
11.	0.3 dm	

Volume and surface area of cylinders

Name _____

Date _____

If r is the radius of the base and h is the height of a cylinder, then

$$V = \pi r^2 h$$

where V is the volume.

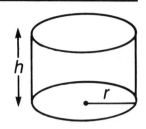

Find the volume of each cylinder given the following. Use 3.14 for π.

	r	h	V
1.	2 m	10 m	125.6 m³
2.	8 cm	14 cm	
3.	11 dm	22 dm	
4.	16 mm	20 mm	
5.	4.8 cm	5.6 cm	

The surface area of a cylinder is the sum of the areas of a rectangle and two circles.

$$S = 2\pi r^2 + 2\pi rh$$

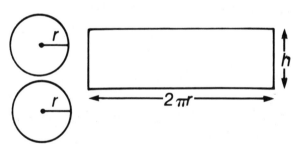

Find the surface area of each cylinder given the following. Use 3.14 for π.

	r	h	S
6.	5 m	10 m	
7.	4 cm	18 cm	
8.	8 dm	22 dm	
9.	12 dkm	30 dkm	
10.	10 mm	50 mm	

Volume of cones and spheres

Name _____

Date _____

If r is the radius of the base of a cone and h is the height, then

$V = \frac{1}{3}\pi r^2 h$ where V is the volume.

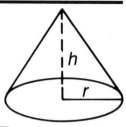

Find the volume of each cone given the following. Use 3.14 for π.

	r	h	V
1.	4.2 m	11.8 m	217.86576 m³
2.	6.2 dm	8.1 dm	
3.	5.1 cm	20 cm	
4.	11 m	30 m	
5.	15 mm	26 mm	

If r is the radius of a sphere, then

$$V = \frac{4}{3}\pi r^3$$

where V is the volume.

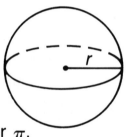

Find the volume of each sphere given the following. Use 3.14 for π.

	r	V
6.	1.2 cm	
7.	3.3 dkm	
8.	0.36 m	
9.	4.2 dm	
10.	3.6 cm	
11.	2.4 mm	

Volume and surface area of cylinders   Name _____

Date _____

If r is the radius of the base and h is the height of a cylinder, then

$$V = \pi r^2 h$$

where V is the volume.

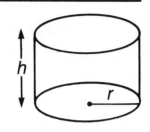

Find the volume of each cylinder given the following. Use 3.14 for π.

	r	h	V
1.	2 cm	8 cm	100.48 cm^3
2.	4 dm	7 dm	
3.	5 m	14 m	
4.	3 cm	4.5 cm	
5.	6 dm	7 dm	

The surface area of a cylinder is the sum of the areas of a rectangle and two circles.

$$S = 2\pi r^2 + 2\pi rh$$

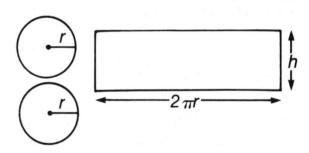

Find the surface area of each cylinder given the following. Use 3.14 for π.

	r	h	S
6.	1 m	25 m	
7.	8 cm	12 cm	
8.	9 dm	20 dm	
9.	7 mm	29 mm	
10.	12 cm	21 cm	

Volume of cones and spheres

Name _____

Date _____

If *r* is the radius of the base of a cone and *h* is the height, then

$V = \frac{1}{3}\pi r^2 h$ where *V* is the volume.

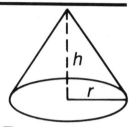

Find the volume of each cone given the following. Use 3.14 for π.

	r	*h*	*V*
1.	1.3 dm	5.4 dm	9.55188 dm³
2.	2.1 m	3.5 m	
3.	10 cm	33 cm	
4.	15 mm	15 mm	
5.	9 km	50 km	

If *r* is the radius of a sphere, then

$$V = \frac{4}{3}\pi r^3$$

where *V* is the volume.

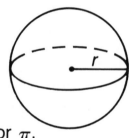

Find the volume of each sphere given the following. Use 3.14 for π.

	r	*V*
6.	0.12 km	
7.	0.21 cm	
8.	0.3 m	
9.	4.5 dm	
10.	5.4 m	
11.	4.8 cm	

ANSWERS

Page 1   **1.** 125 ft³, 150 ft²   **2.** 12,167 yd³, 3174 yd²   **3.** 1728 in.³, 864 in.²
4. 21,952 in.³, 4704 in.²   **5.** 10,648 ft³, 2904 ft²
6. $\frac{1}{64}$ in.³, $\frac{3}{8}$ in.²   **7.** $\frac{8}{27}$ ft³, $\frac{8}{3}$ ft²   **8.** $\frac{27}{64}$ yd³, $\frac{27}{8}$ yd²
9. $\frac{125}{4096}$ in.³, $\frac{75}{128}$ in.²   **10.** $\frac{125}{216}$ ft³, $\frac{25}{6}$ ft²   **11.** $\frac{27}{512}$
in.³, $\frac{27}{32}$ in.²   **12.** $\frac{343}{512}$ in.³, $\frac{147}{32}$ in.²   **13.** $10\frac{37}{216}$
in.³, $28\frac{1}{6}$ in.²   **14.** $3\frac{1675}{1728}$ yd³, $15\frac{1}{24}$ yd²
15. $34\frac{21}{64}$ ft³, $63\frac{3}{8}$ ft²   **16.** 5 yd, 125 yd³
17. 4 in., 64 in.³   **18.** 2 ft, 24 ft²   **19.** 3 in.,
54 in.²   **20.** 2 ft, 8 ft³

Page 2   **1.** 729 m³, 486 m²   **2.** 2197 cm³,
1014 cm²   **3.** 343,000 mm³, 29,400 mm²
4. 2744 cm³, 1176 cm²   **5.** 0.343 mm³,
2.94 mm²   **6.** 1.728 cm³, 8.64 cm²
7. 54.872 m³, 86.64 m²   **8.** 778.688 dm³,
507.84 dm²   **9.** 3 cm, 27 cm³   **10.** 5 cm,
150 cm²

Page 3   **1.** 4913 in.³, 1734 in.²   **2.** 1331 in.³,
726 in.²   **3.** 24,389 ft³, 5046 ft²   **4.** 64,000 in.³,
9600 in.²   **5.** 15,625 yd³, 3750 yd²
6. 1,000,000 in.³, 60,000 in.²   **7.** 27 yd³, 54 yd²
8. $\frac{125}{4096}$ in.³, $\frac{75}{128}$ in.²   **9.** $\frac{27}{64}$ in.³, $\frac{27}{8}$ in.²   **10.** $\frac{125}{1728}$
ft³, $\frac{25}{24}$ ft²   **11.** $\frac{729}{4096}$ in.³, $\frac{243}{128}$ in.²   **12.** $\frac{125}{216}$ yd³,
$\frac{25}{6}$ yd²   **13.** $\frac{343}{1728}$ ft³, $\frac{49}{24}$ ft²   **14.** $\frac{1}{64}$ yd³, $\frac{3}{8}$ yd²
15. $465\frac{31}{64}$ in.³, $360\frac{3}{8}$ in.²   **16.** $18\frac{26}{27}$ yd³, $42\frac{2}{3}$ yd²
17. $107\frac{11}{64}$ ft³, $135\frac{3}{8}$ ft²   **18.** 8 ft, 512 ft³
19. 13 in., 2197 in.³   **20.** 4 yd, 96 yd²

Page 4   **1.** 64 m³, 96 m²   **2.** 85,184 cm³,
11,616 cm²   **3.** 50,653 mm³, 8214 mm²
4. 0.008 cm³, 0.24 cm²   **5.** 389.017 m³,
319.74 m²   **6.** 32.768 mm³, 61.44 mm²
7. 68.921 cm³, 100.86 cm²   **8.** 185.193 m³,
194.94 m²   **9.** 12 mm, 1728 mm³   **10.** 8 cm,
384 cm²

Page 5   **1.** 3375 in.³, 1350 in.²
2. 79,507 yd³, 11,094 yd²   **3.** 216 ft³, 216 ft²
4. 5832 ft³, 1944 ft²   **5.** 729,000 yd³,
48,600 yd²   **6.** 27,000 in.³, 5400 in.²   **7.** $\frac{27}{4096}$
in.³, $\frac{27}{128}$ in.²   **8.** $\frac{343}{1728}$ yd³, $\frac{49}{24}$ yd²   **9.** $\frac{1331}{1728}$ ft³,
$\frac{121}{24}$ ft²   **10.** $\frac{125}{512}$ in.³, $\frac{75}{128}$ in.²   **11.** $\frac{343}{4096}$ in.³, $\frac{147}{128}$ in.²
12. $\frac{27}{64}$ ft³, $\frac{27}{8}$ ft²   **13.** $\frac{125}{216}$ yd³, $\frac{25}{6}$ yd²
14. $5\frac{23}{64}$ yd³, $18\frac{3}{8}$ yd²   **15.** $58\frac{95}{512}$ in.³,
$90\frac{3}{32}$ in.²   **16.** $16\frac{503}{729}$ yd³, $39\frac{5}{27}$ yd²
17. 14 in., 2744 in.³   **18.** 6 yd, 216 yd³
19. 3 in., 54 in.²   **20.** 2 in., 24 in.²

Page 6   **1.** 42,875 m³, 7350 m²
2. 9261 cm³, 2646 cm²   **3.** 74,088 mm³,
10,584 mm²   **4.** 103.823 cm³, 132.54 cm²
5. 132.651 m³, 156.06 m²   **6.** 421.875 cm³,
337.5 cm²   **7.** 0.512 m³, 3.84 m²
8. 250.047 mm³, 238.14 mm²   **9.** 10 cm,
1000 cm³   **10.** 7 cm, 294 cm²

Page 7   **1.** 68,921 ft³, 10,086 ft²
2. 8000 yd³, 2400 yd²   **3.** 54,872 ft³, 8664 ft²
4. 216,000 yd³, 21,600 yd²   **5.** 8 in.³, 24 in.²
6. 32,768 in.³, 6144 in.²   **7.** $\frac{729}{4096}$ in.³, $\frac{243}{128}$ in.²
8. $\frac{1}{64}$ yd³, $\frac{3}{8}$ yd²   **9.** $\frac{1}{1728}$ ft³, $\frac{1}{24}$ ft²   **10.** $\frac{125}{216}$ ft³,
$\frac{25}{6}$ ft²   **11.** $\frac{125}{1728}$ ft³, $\frac{25}{24}$ ft²   **12.** $\frac{343}{729}$ yd³, $\frac{98}{27}$ yd²
13. $\frac{27}{512}$ in.³, $\frac{27}{32}$ in.²   **14.** $52\frac{47}{64}$ yd³, $84\frac{3}{8}$ yd²
15. $4\frac{149}{512}$ in.³, $15\frac{27}{32}$ in.²   **16.** $181\frac{26}{27}$ ft³, $192\frac{2}{3}$ ft²
17. 15 in., 3375 in.³   **18.** 1 ft, 6 ft²   **19.** 4 in.,
96 in.²   **20.** 11 ft, 1331 ft³

Page 8   **1.** 512 m³, 384 m²   **2.** 35,937 cm³,
6534 cm²   **3.** 19,683 mm³, 4374 mm²
4. 79.507 m³, 110.94 m²   **5.** 0.125 mm³,
1.5 mm²   **6.** 21.952 cm³, 47.04 cm²
7. 830.584 mm³, 530.16 mm²   **8.** 2 m, 8 m³
9. 9 cm, 729 cm³   **10.** 10 cm, 600 cm²

Page 9   **1.** 1000 ft³, 600 ft²   **2.** 29,791 yd³,
5766 yd²   **3.** 343 in.³, 294 in.²   **4.** 59,319 ft³,
9126 ft²   **5.** 125,000 yd³, 15,000 yd²
6. 729,000 in.³, 48,600 in.²   **7.** $\frac{27}{64}$ yd³, $\frac{27}{8}$ yd²
8. $\frac{1}{216}$ yd³, $\frac{1}{6}$ yd²   **9.** $\frac{343}{512}$ in.³, $\frac{147}{32}$ in.²
10. $\frac{1331}{4096}$ in.³, $\frac{363}{128}$ in.²   **11.** $\frac{1331}{1728}$ ft³, $\frac{121}{24}$ ft²
12. $\frac{343}{1728}$ ft³, $\frac{49}{24}$ ft²   **13.** $\frac{1}{64}$ yd³, $\frac{3}{8}$ yd²   **14.** $12\frac{19}{27}$
ft³, $32\frac{2}{3}$ ft²   **15.** $20\frac{51}{64}$ in.³, $45\frac{3}{8}$ in.²   **16.** $6\frac{35}{216}$
yd³, $20\frac{1}{6}$ yd²   **17.** 1 yd, 1 yd³   **18.** 7 in., 343 in.³
19. 11 yd, 726 yd²   **20.** 5 ft, 150 ft²

Page 10   **1.** 17,576 cm³, 4056 cm²
2. 4096 m³, 1536 m²   **3.** 39,304 cm³, 6936 cm²
4. 9.261 cm³, 26.46 cm²   **5.** 0.216 m³, 2.16 m²
6. 262.144 mm³, 245.76 mm²   **7.** 551.368 cm³,
403.44 cm²   **8.** 389.017 m³, 319.74 m²
9. 11 cm, 1331 cm³   **10.** 9 m, 486 m²

Page 11   **1.** 60 ft³, 94 ft²   **2.** 3240 in.³,
1428 in.²   **3.** $\frac{5}{24}$ ft³, $\frac{157}{72}$ ft²   **4.** $14\frac{35}{128}$ in.³,
$36\frac{7}{8}$ in.²   **5.** $62\frac{1}{36}$ yd³, $111\frac{13}{36}$ yd²   **6.** $7\frac{7}{8}$ ft³,
$25\frac{1}{2}$ ft²   **7.** 50 in., 7096 in.²   **8.** 16 ft, 1468 ft²

71

Page 12   **1.** 126 cm³, 162 cm²
2. 79,475 m³, 14,110 m²   **3.** 60.844 cm³,
124.72 cm²   **4.** 0.088536 m³, 1.2652 m²
5. 289.788 dm³, 285.52 dm²   **6.** 12.74 mm³,
35.98 mm²   **7.** 9 m, 454 m²

Page 13   **1.** 56 in.³, 100 in.²   **2.** 64 ft³,
112 ft²   **3.** 15,120 in.³, 3996 in.²   **4.** $\frac{15}{128}$ in.³,
$\frac{13}{8}$ in.²   **5.** $18\frac{1}{3}$ ft³, $43\frac{19}{36}$ ft²   **6.** $49\frac{7}{12}$ yd³,
$82\frac{25}{36}$ yd²   **7.** $113\frac{29}{32}$ in.³, $165\frac{3}{8}$ in.²   **8.** 32 ft,
3472 ft²   **9.** 12 yd, 664 yd²

Page 14   **1.** 3588 m³, 1462 m²
2. 69.006 cm³, 103.42 cm²   **3.** 0.201474 m³,
2.139 m²   **4.** 9.828 cm³, 29.94 cm²
5. 38.808 m³, 72.68 m²   **6.** 6 cm, 516 cm²
7. 7 m, 320 m²

Page 15   **1.** 30 ft³, 82 ft²   **2.** 162 yd³,
198 yd²   **3.** 17,024 in.³, 4528 in.²   **4.** $\frac{1}{27}$ ft³, $\frac{7}{9}$ ft²
5. $52\frac{65}{128}$ in.³, $88\frac{3}{8}$ in.²   **6.** $39\frac{65}{72}$ ft³, $74\frac{1}{36}$ ft²
7. $121\frac{1}{3}$ yd³, $165\frac{2}{9}$ yd²   **8.** 18 in., 2292 in.²

Page 16   **1.** 21,756 cm³, 4802 cm²
2. 58.52 m³, 102.04 m²   **3.** 0.12144 cm³,
1.5526 cm²   **4.** 21.756 m³, 53.2 m²
5. 42.688 mm³, 78.52 mm²   **6.** 7 mm,
1062 mm²   **7.** 43 m, 3598 m²

Page 17   **1.** 84 ft³, 122 ft²   **2.** 24 yd³, 70 yd²
3. 9537 in.³, 3230 in.²   **4.** $\frac{5}{12}$ ft³, $\frac{121}{36}$ ft²
5. $93\frac{1}{3}$ yd³, $124\frac{7}{9}$ yd²   **6.** $33\frac{51}{128}$ in.³, $79\frac{3}{8}$ in.²
7. $35\frac{7}{18}$ ft³, $66\frac{8}{9}$ ft²   **8.** 8 in., 670 in.²   **9.** 23 ft,
3370 ft²

Page 18   **1.** 3864 cm³, 1532 cm²
2. 91.854 m³, 153.9 m²   **3.** 0.0148 m³,
0.3834 m²   **4.** 81.673 cm³, 126.22 cm²
5. 84.952 mm³, 117.7 mm²   **6.** 25 cm,
1866 cm²   **7.** 3.7 mm, 282.22 mm²

Page 19   **1.** 48 yd³, 92 yd²   **2.** 168 ft³,
188 ft²   **3.** 9384 in.³, 3076 in.²   **4.** $\frac{105}{512}$ in.³,
$\frac{149}{64}$ in.²   **5.** $21\frac{9}{16}$ yd³, $47\frac{2}{3}$ yd²   **6.** $61\frac{1}{4}$ ft³,
$111\frac{17}{24}$ ft²   **7.** $44\frac{59}{64}$ in.³, $80\frac{5}{16}$ in.²   **8.** 5 ft, 790 ft²

Page 20   **1.** 18,018 m³, 4982 m²
2. 140.544 cm³, 172.96 cm²   **3.** 0.080401 m³,
1.1302 m²   **4.** 39.48 cm³, 83.54 cm²
5. 402.408 mm³, 335.88 mm²   **6.** 17 mm,
1086 mm²   **7.** 32 cm, 5008 cm²

Page 21   **1.** 304 gal   **2.** 540,000 yd³
3. 300 ft³   **4.** 156 in.³   **5.** 149.6 gal

Page 22   **1.** 490 ft³   **2.** 1440 in.²   **3.** 8 gal
4. 5400 in.²   **5.** 84.15 gal

Page 23   **1.** 535 gal   **2.** 150,000 yd³
3. 400 ft³   **4.** $183\frac{1}{3}$ in.³   **5.** 261.8 gal

Page 24   **1.** 312 ft³   **2.** 1192 in.²   **3.** 4 gal
4. 3750 in.²   **5.** 37.4 gal

Page 25   **1.** 342 gal   **2.** 150,000 yd³
3. 157.5 ft³   **4.** 330 in.³   **5.** 145.86 gal

Page 26   **1.** 220.5 ft³   **2.** 2560 in.²   **3.** 8 gal
4. 2400 in.²   **5.** 28.05 gal

Page 27   **1.** 292.5 gal   **2.** 270,000 yd³
3. 500 ft³   **4.** $322\frac{2}{3}$ in.³   **5.** 112.2 gal

Page 28   **1.** 325 ft³   **2.** 1200 in.²   **3.** 9 gal
4. 1944 in.²   **5.** 11.22 gal

Page 29   **1.** 500 gal   **2.** 119,700 yd³
3. 125 ft³   **4.** 455 in.³   **5.** 261.8 gal

Page 30   **1.** $394\frac{1}{3}$ ft³   **2.** 2696 in.²   **3.** 4 gal
4. 864 in.²   **5.** 22.44 gal

Page 31   **1.** 168 ft³   **2.** 840 in.³   **3.** $10\frac{2}{3}$ yd³
4. $5\frac{1}{4}$ ft³   **5.** 11 in.   **6.** 20 in.   **7.** 150 ft³
8. 576 in.³   **9.** $3\frac{1}{2}$ ft³   **10.** $3\frac{1}{2}$ yd³   **11.** 6 ft
12. 7 in.

Page 32   **1.** 180 mm³   **2.** 5.145 cm³
3. 1.248 m³   **4.** 15 cm   **5.** 286 m³
6. 1.488 cm³   **7.** 6.93 m³   **8.** 5 cm

Page 33   **1.** 351 yd³   **2.** 385 in.³   **3.** $21\frac{2}{3}$ ft³
4. 14 yd³   **5.** 11 ft   **6.** 13 in.   **7.** 273 in.³
8. 456 ft³   **9.** $8\frac{5}{27}$ ft³   **10.** $4\frac{5}{18}$ yd³   **11.** 5 in.
12. 8 ft

Page 34   **1.** 952 cm³   **2.** 29.078 mm³
3. 7.038 cm³   **4.** 22 cm   **5.** 182 m³
6. 8.54 cm³   **7.** 26.568 cm³   **8.** 13 cm

Page 35   **1.** 756 in.³   **2.** 245 ft³   **3.** $8\frac{1}{8}$ yd³
4. $11\frac{11}{12}$ ft³   **5.** 5 in.   **6.** 560 ft³   **7.** 304 in.³
8. $6\frac{3}{16}$ in.³   **9.** $16\frac{23}{27}$ ft³   **10.** 13 in.

Page 36   **1.** 675 mm³   **2.** 12.096 m³
3. 110.565 cm³   **4.** 14 mm   **5.** 7 cm
6. 408 cm³   **7.** 5.59 cm³   **8.** 12.852 m³
9. 5 mm   **10.** 26 cm

Page 37   **1.** 405 yd³   **2.** 264 in.³   **3.** $18\frac{3}{4}$ ft³
4. $3\frac{1}{2}$ yd³   **5.** 9 in.   **6.** 7 ft   **7.** 1225 in.³
8. 208 ft³   **9.** $61\frac{7}{8}$ in.³   **10.** $6\frac{5}{12}$ yd³   **11.** 7 in.

Page 38   **1.** 1326 cm³   **2.** 59.262 mm³
3. 37.31 m³   **4.** 14 m   **5.** 425 cm³
6. 37.23 cm³   **7.** 15.249 mm³   **8.** 18 cm
9. 19 mm

Page 39   **1.** 360 ft³   **2.** 702 in.³   **3.** $5\frac{5}{12}$ yd³
4. $13\frac{11}{24}$ ft³   **5.** 12 in.   **6.** 3 ft   **7.** 350 ft³
8. 276 ft³   **9.** $12\frac{3}{8}$ in.³   **10.** $6\frac{17}{18}$ yd³   **11.** 15 in.
12. 42 ft

Page 40   **1.** 931 mm³   **2.** 2.457 m³
3. 21.708 cm³   **4.** 16 m   **5.** 182 cm³
6. 24.96 m³   **7.** 12.493 cm³   **8.** 43 cm

Page 41   **1.** 110 mm, 35 mm, $\frac{110}{35}$, 3.14
2. 144 mm, 46 mm, $\frac{144}{46}$, 3.13   **3.** 157 mm,
50 mm, $\frac{157}{50}$, 3.14

Page 42   **1.** 40 mm, 20 mm, 125.6 mm,
1256 mm²   **2.** 48 mm, 24 mm, 150.72 mm,
1808.64 mm²   **3.** 28 mm, 14 mm, 87.92 mm,
615.44 mm²

Page 43   **1.** 72 mm, 23 mm, $\frac{72}{23}$, 3.13
2. 132 mm, 42 mm, $\frac{132}{42}$, 3.14   **3.** 101 mm,
32 mm, $\frac{101}{32}$, 3.16

Page 44   **1.** 40 mm, 20 mm, 125.6 mm,
1256 mm²   **2.** 26 mm, 13 mm, 81.64 mm,
530.66 mm²   **3.** 35 mm, 17.5 mm, 109.9 mm,
961.625 mm²

Page 45   **1.** 72 mm, 23 mm, $\frac{72}{23}$, 3.13
2. 97 mm, 31 mm, $\frac{97}{31}$, 3.13   **3.** 151 mm,
48 mm, $\frac{151}{48}$, 3.15

Page 46   **1.** 32 mm, 16 mm, 100.48 mm,
803.84 mm²   **2.** 50 mm, 25 mm, 157 mm,
1962.5 mm²   **3.** 41 mm, 20.5 mm, 128.74 mm,
1319.585 mm²

Page 47   **1.** 53 mm, 17 mm, $\frac{53}{17}$, 3.12
2. 144 mm, 46 mm, $\frac{144}{46}$, 3.13   **3.** 119 mm,
38 mm, $\frac{119}{38}$, 3.13

Page 48   **1.** 20 mm, 10 mm, 62.8 mm,
314 mm²   **2.** 42 mm, 21 mm, 131.88 mm,
1384.74 mm²   **3.** 33 mm, 16.5 mm,
103.62 mm, 854.865 mm²

Page 49   **1.** 154 mm, 49 mm, $\frac{154}{49}$, 3.14
2. 47 mm, 15 mm, $\frac{47}{15}$, 3.13   **3.** 110 mm,
35 mm, $\frac{110}{35}$, 3.14

Page 50   **1.** 29 mm, 14.5 mm, 91.06 mm,
660.185 mm²   **2.** 30 mm, 15 mm, 94.2 mm,
706.5 mm²   **3.** 44 mm, 22 mm, 138.16 mm,
1519.76 mm²

Page 51   **1.** 42, 132, 1386   **2.** 126, 396,
12,474   **3.** $11\frac{5}{11}$, 36, $103\frac{1}{11}$ **4.** $6\frac{4}{11}$, 20, $31\frac{9}{11}$
5. $16\frac{6}{11}$, 52, $215\frac{1}{11}$ **6.** 15, 94.2, 706.5   **7.** 4.1,
25.748, 52.7834   **8.** 6.2, 38.936, 120.7016
9. 3.5, 21.98, 38.465   **10.** 0.37, 2.3236,
0.429866

Page 52   **1.** 6   **2.** $1.10   **3.** 1   **4.** $4.00
5. 471 in.², 706.5 in.², party pizza

Page 53   **1.** 11, $69\frac{1}{7}$, $380\frac{2}{7}$ **2.** 22, $138\frac{2}{7}$,
$1521\frac{1}{7}$ **3.** $5\frac{1}{11}$, 32, $81\frac{5}{11}$ **4.** $9\frac{1}{3}$, $58\frac{2}{3}$, $273\frac{7}{9}$
5. $6\frac{2}{9}$, $39\frac{1}{9}$, $121\frac{55}{81}$ **6.** 56, 175.84, 2461.76
7. 52, 163.28, 2122.64   **8.** 12.6, 39.564,
124.6266   **9.** 16.4, 51.496, 211.1336
10. 0.86, 2.7004, 0.580586

Page 54   **1.** 25 in.², 78.5 in.²   **2.** 144 in.²,
452.16 in.²   **3.** 5   **4.** $6.90   **5.** yes

Page 55   **1.** 28, 88, 616   **2.** 42, 264, 5544
3. $10\frac{1}{2}$, 33, $86\frac{5}{8}$ **4.** $13\frac{1}{2}$, $42\frac{3}{7}$, $143\frac{11}{56}$ **5.** $25\frac{1}{5}$,
$79\frac{1}{5}$, $498\frac{24}{25}$ **6.** 98, 307.72, 7539.14   **7.** 4.2,
26.376, 55.3896   **8.** 5.6, 35.168, 98.4704
9. 17.8, 55.892, 248.7194   **10.** 15.2, 47.728,
181.3664

Page 56   **1.** 49 in.², 153.86 in.²   **2.** 144 in.²,
452.16 in.²   **3.** 76.98 in.²   **4.** $3.575
5. 150.72 in.²   **6.** 2.73\frac{1}{3}$ **7.** Lita, Megan, and
Mike

Page 57   **1.** 5, $31\frac{3}{7}$, $78\frac{4}{7}$ **2.** 4, $25\frac{1}{7}$, $50\frac{2}{7}$
3. $10\frac{2}{5}$, $32\frac{24}{35}$, $84\frac{172}{175}$ **4.** $10\frac{1}{2}$, 33, $86\frac{5}{8}$ **5.** $5\frac{1}{4}$,
$16\frac{1}{2}$, $21\frac{21}{32}$ **6.** 6, 18.84, 28.26   **7.** 34, 106.76,
907.46   **8.** 4.2, 26.376, 55.3896   **9.** 1.5, 9.42,
7.065   **10.** 3.6, 22.608, 40.6944

Page 58   **1.** 25 in.², 78.5 in.²   **2.** 225 in.²,
706.5 in.²   **3.** 2   **4.** $37.70

Page 59   **1.** 7, 44, 154   **2.** 14, 88, 616
3. $1\frac{3}{11}$, 4, $1\frac{3}{11}$ **4.** 21, 66, $346\frac{1}{2}$ **5.** $10\frac{2}{11}$, 32,
$81\frac{5}{11}$ **6.** 10, 31.4, 78.5   **7.** 18, 56.52, 254.34
8. 11, 69.08, 379.94   **9.** 16, 100.48, 803.84
10. 4.2, 26.376, 55.3896

Page 60   **1.** 78.5 in.²   **2.** 113.04 in.²
3. 452.16 in.²   **4.** 706.5 in.²   **5.** 4   **6.** 9

Page 61   **1.** 942 cm³   **2.** 1538.6 mm³
3. 7686.72 m³   **4.** 31,400 cm³   **5.** 57.933 dm³
6. 565.2 m²   **7.** 1796.08 cm²   **8.** 251.2 dm²
9. 15,072 cm²   **10.** 3717.76 mm²

Page 62   **1.** 2110.08 mm³   **2.** 4239 cm³
3. 12,001.08 dm³   **4.** 1017.36 m³
5. 753.6 cm³   **6.** 3052.08 m³   **7.** 14,130 cm³
8. 113.04 cm³   **9.** 904.32 dm³
10. 7234.56 mm³   **11.** 14.13 m³

Page 63   **1.** 9.4985 cm³   **2.** 150.72 m³
3. 90.432 dm³   **4.** 197.82 m³   **5.** 1020.5 mm³
6. 747.32 mm²   **7.** 1105.28 dm²
8. 119.8852 dkm²   **9.** 47.4768 m²
10. 1884 cm²

Page 64   **1.** 4474.5 mm³   **2.** 75.36 m³
3. 753.6 cm³   **4.** 19.0755 dm³
5. 4823.04 cm³   **6.** 14.13 cm³
7. 38.77272 m³   **8.** 7234.56 dm³
9. 57.87648 cm³   **10.** 904.32 mm³
11. 113.04 cm³

Page 65   **1.** 18,149.2 dkm³
2. 1838.9096 cm³   **3.** 4.644688 mm³
4. 0.2512 m³   **5.** 3768 cm³   **6.** 326.56 m²
7. 747.32 dm²   **8.** 131.88 cm²   **9.** 0.3768 mm²
10. 22,608 m²

Page 66   **1.** 11,539.5 cm³   **2.** 414.48 dm³
3. 1356.48 cm³   **4.** 3918.72 mm³
5. 351.68 m³   **6.** 24.41664 dm³
7. 2224.96632 cm³   **8.** 0.01413 m³
9. 82.40616 cm³   **10.** 0.05787648 m³
11. 0.11304 dm³

Page 67   **1.** 125.6 m³   **2.** 2813.44 cm³
3. 8358.68 dm³   **4.** 16,076.8 mm³
5. 405.13536 cm³   **6.** 471 m²   **7.** 552.64 cm²
8. 1507.2 dm²   **9.** 3165.12 dkm²
10. 3768 mm²

Page 68   **1.** 217.86576 m³
2. 325.89432 dm³   **3.** 544.476 cm³
4. 3799.4 m³   **5.** 6123 mm³   **6.** 7.23456 cm³
7. 150.45624 dkm³   **8.** 0.19533312 m³
9. 310.18176 dm³   **10.** 195.33312 cm³
11. 57.87648 mm³

Page 69   **1.** 100.48 cm³   **2.** 351.68 dm³
3. 1099 m³   **4.** 127.17 cm³   **5.** 791.28 dm³
6. 163.28 m²   **7.** 1004.8 cm²   **8.** 1639.08 dm²
9. 1582.56 mm²   **10.** 2486.88 cm²

Page 70   **1.** 9.55188 dm³   **2.** 16.1553 m³
3. 3454 cm³   **4.** 3532.5 mm³   **5.** 4239 km³
6. 0.00723456 km³   **7.** 0.03877272 cm³
8. 0.11304 m³   **9.** 381.51 dm³
10. 659.24928 m³   **11.** 463.01184 cm³